LIFE AND COMPLETE WORKS
OF MICHAEL BRUCE

Kinnesswood and Kinross do well to cherish the memory of Michael Bruce. He is the most lovable poet in all our literature. His characteristic notes are naturalness and cheerfulness. He is no fireside poet: the Lomond Hill was his mountain of the Lord, rising over the mountaintops; he was, and is, the poet of Lochleven. There is no sorrow in his song; even death is only a brief parting, soon over. He is often jubilant. As long as praise is a part of adoration, his hymns will be sung. See letter from Mr. J. LOGIE ROBERTSON, page 294

Bruce's poems have great merit; they are chaste, classical, and often exhibit the highest beauties of poetry. The 'Elegy,' which was written when he was a-dying is a masterpiece.—THOS. ROBERTSON, D.D.

Dalmeny Manse.
   22nd February, 1791.

LIFE AND COMPLETE
WORKS OF
MICHAEL BRUCE

POET OF LOCH LEVEN

AUTHOR OF THE "ODE TO THE CUCKOO"
AND OTHER POEMS AND PARAPHRASES

THE COTTAGE EDITION

BY

JOHN GUTHRIE BARNET

ILLUSTRATED

LONDON

CHAS. J. THYNNE & JARVIS, LTD.
WHITEFRIARS STREET, FLEET STREET, E.C.4

1927

Ah, what a paradise begins with life, and what a wilderness the knowledge of the world discloses ! Surely the Garden of Eden was nothing more than our first parents' entrance upon life, and the loss of it their knowledge of the world.—JOHN CLARE.

I expect to pass through this life but once. If, therefore, there is any kindness I can show or any good I can do to any fellow-being, let me do it now, let me not defer or neglect it, for I shall not pass this way again.—A. B. HEGEMAN.

Printed in Great Britain by
M. F. Robinson & Co., Ltd., at The Library Press, Lowestoft.

PREFACE

In almost every biography of Michael Bruce we are reminded that the poet had taken the place he holds in our national literature before he had much more than completed his twenty-first year. His career was a remarkable example of the way in which native genius will triumph over all discouraging circumstances. Although he was of the humblest origin, thanks to his parents and friends he was highly educated, and wrote lyric poetry which the highest artifice could not hope to emulate. It was in the familiar things of the country-side, his radiant faith and full knowledge of the Scriptures, that he found his inspiration, and he touched them in simple words to a beauty which may be compared with that of our finest poets.

The new era in the posthumous fame of Bruce dates to the time when Dr. Mackelvie published his " Life of Bruce," in 1837, creating what was known as the Logan-Bruce controversy, which was carried on for nearly a century. Such was the interest awakened in the subject that it was impossible to procure any copies of the life and works of Michael Bruce till they were published by Dr. Grosart in 1865. After another interval of thirty years, the Rev. Wm. Stephen of Kelty published a very able book on the poet's life and writings, and it was not long before this edition was exhausted.

In 1914, the " Life and Complete Works of Michael Bruce " by James Mackenzie, F.S.A.S., appeared, and so thorough and exhaustive was the work done by Mr. Mackenzie, that no biographer following him could give a fuller or better account of the life of the poet than he has done in his book, which is known as the Kinnesswood Edition. This edition soon ran out of print, and it is with a desire to fill up the gap and keep alive the memory of Michael Bruce that I have been induced to attempt a further edition, which might be known as the " Cottage Edition," as a full account of the Cottage Endowment Fund will be included in the volume.

I have only to add that the task of re-tracing the pathetic, yet ever-inspiring life-story of Michael Bruce, and renewing acquaintance with his writings has afforded me the greatest pleasure, in which I hope the reader will also participate.

J. G. B.

DULWICH,
    December, 1926

INTRODUCTION

Many years ago the Michael Bruce Trust was formed to preserve and keep in repair the birth-place of Michael Bruce, " Loch Leven's gentle poet," and as it was decided at a meeting of the trustees and other admirers of the poet held at Kinross on October 13th, 1926, to inaugurate a commemoration service at the poet's birth-place, and offer prizes to each school within the area for an essay on the Life and Works of Michael Bruce, I felt impelled to bring out the present, which may be described as The Cottage Edition, hoping the book may be of some service to the school children competing for the prizes. The original edition of Bruce's poems, now a very rare and valuable book, was published in 1770, and since then over twenty books on Michael Bruce by various writers have appeared, the last one appearing in 1914, the most complete and finest of all, the title of which is : " Life and Complete Works of Michael Bruce ; Poet of Loch Leven. Author of the ' Ode to the Cuckoo,' and other poems. The Kinnesswood Edition. By James Mackenzie, F.S.A.S. Illustrated." It was the fullest and most thorough collection of Michael Bruce's poems that had yet been made, and the book was highly valued by every one who wished to have well-instructed opinions on the merits and authenticity of the poems concerned.

At the meeting of the Trustees held in October, 1926, Mr. R. S. Young, Clerk to the Trust, made feeling reference to the loss the Trust had sustained through the death of Mr. James Mackenzie, F.S.A.S., which occurred very shortly after the previous meeting in April, 1925. I was present at the 1925 meeting, and shall never forget the happy spirit which permeated the proceedings. Mr. Mackenzie presided, and as usual threw himself heart and soul into what was for him a labour of love. He has left behind him many fragrant memories as a kindly, God-fearing and lovable friend. I think, however, it will be by his devotion to the aim he set himself out to accomplish, and which he so nobly carried out—to preserve for all time the birth-place of Michael Bruce, as a public heritage —that his name will always be held in affectionate remembrance around the shores of the Loch he loved so well.

The Trustees sent an expression of sincere sympathy to Mrs. Mackenzie and her family in their bereavement, recognizing " the deep gratitude which all who appreciate the life and work of Michael Bruce owe to Mr. Mackenzie for all his efforts." I had a characteristic letter from Mr. Mackenzie on February 14th, 1922 (Valentine's Day, by the way), in which he wrote : " Well, I am still on for what naturally concerns us both, viz. Michael Bruce." He asked me to write and make an appeal through the " Kinross-shire Advertiser," of which I was then Editor-Proprietor for the purpose of raising an Endowment Fund for the permanent preservation and upkeep of Michael Bruce's Cottage. I gave my hearty consent to this, and acted accordingly. Not only in the local paper, but in the newspapers of neighbouring counties did the appeal appear, and some daily newspapers, including the " Glasgow Herald," drew attention to the matter. Contributions, exceeding all expectations, were received from admirers of the poet at home and abroad, accompanied by interesting correspondence, and we feel it is incumbent upon us to publish the appeal as well as a list of the contributors and some of the correspondence, which will be found at the end of the volume, paying tribute to the poetic genius of Michael Bruce. Our aim was to raise £300, but in the end we reached nearly £400, and Mr. Mackenzie wrote to me that it was no small joy to him to know that what he had set out to achieve was now an accomplished fact. We feel sure that the joy to which Mr. Mackenzie gave expression will be shared by all who fully realise what Michael Bruce and his writings signify.

In the course of our narrative we shall have occasion to touch upon various aspects of Michael Bruce's life and writings, but the one outstanding feature, we think, was his gentle and amiable character, which commanded the affection and regard of his fellow students, as well as persons in all spheres of life during his short earthly career, and the reason of this is revealed in the secret joy which he carried about in his heart—that "secret of the Lord which is with them that fear Him." This secret may be acquired in the same simple way of faith by young and old in all ages, and if it were generally held at the present day, at home and throughout the British Empire, a great nation indeed would arise and be the means in God's hands of putting an end to all the turmoil and unrest in the world at the present time. Thousands of our young men carried the secret in their hearts when they went "over the top" in the Great War, and when many of them were suddenly ushered into the presence of Him Who will yet be King of Kings and Lord of Lords. Bruce gave expression to this thought in the following verse from the 18th Paraphrase.

The beam that shines from Sion hill, shall lighten every land ;
The King who reigns in Salem's tow'rs, shall all the world command.

Especially gratifying is it to us to think that the Cottage in which the young poet was born, will remain a perpetual testimony to all coming generations of these everlasting truths, and be a source of encouragement and inspiration to the young generations following, as the paraphrases which Michael Bruce wrote will for ever form songs of praise in all assemblies which meet for the purpose of worshipping God. No one possessed of the secret and spirit which animated the young poet can go about with a heavy countenance, as they are in possession of the true riches of life, such as the poet expressed in his poem on " Heavenly Wisdom " ;—which forms the eleventh Paraphrase, commencing :

> O happy is the man who hears
> Instruction's warning voice ;
> And who celestial wisdom makes
> His early only choice.

So exalted is the truth contained in the eleventh Paraphrase, so rich and glorious, it enriches everything it touches with something of its own distinction. This is the real philosopher's stone ; it transforms everything into spiritual gold. It endows everything with divine quality—our thoughts, our wishes, our affections, our purposes, our actions—it touches everything into gold. And for keeping this truth ever fresh in our memory we owe a deep debt of gratitude to Michael Bruce.

Over half a century ago, when we were at school in Kinross, we committed to memory the " Ode to the Cuckoo " and the 11th Paraphrase, still as fresh in the memory as ever, and with such thoughts in their minds young people are well equipped for the battles and pitfalls in life. It is with a view to awakening such interest among the young that we have undertaken the issue of this volume of the complete works of Michael Bruce, to which all interested may now have access, and now after the lapse of so many years since he died in his twenty-first year, 5th July, 1767, we consider that only a brief sketch of the Poet's life with an appreciation of his Work, is all that is required.

We owe a debt of gratitude to Mrs. James Mackenzie, Edinburgh, for her courtesy and kindness in presenting us with the illustrations which added so greatly to the interest and value of her husband's Kinnesswood Edition of the poet, and thereby this CottageEdition will be greatly enhanced and appreciated.

CONTENTS

xi

CONTENTS

CONTENTS

GOSPEL SONNETS—Original
    (*Adopted in the Paraphrases*)

OLD HYMNS—Improved
    (*With Variations*)

CONTENTS

ILLUSTRATIONS

Sir

The following will inform you that we are in a table-
Condition (if you will excuse the novelty of the Words
which I desire you to take into Consideration I was about
to say a great many fine things on this Subject, but I
find they are all slipt out of my Head. To your Wife
Brother, make the Compliments of yours

Sincerely
Michael Bruce

(1762) Michael Bruce — (1763) Michael Bruce,

Michael Bruce,

FACSIMILE OF BRUCE'S HANDWRITING

1 A Letter from Gairney Bridge. 2. Signatures in Edinburgh University Album.

LIFE OF MICHAEL BRUCE

Chapter I

PARENTAGE AND HOME LIFE

MICHAEL BRUCE was the fifth of a family of eight, and was born in the village of Kinnesswood, Kinross-shire, 17th March, 1746, and had rather a delicate constitution. The cottage in which he was born is fully described elsewhere in this book. Nothing is more fascinating in nature than the delight and wonder of a child when it first discovers a little bird's nest in some out-of-the-way hedgerow or bush in the country, and to young and old alike there is this same fascination in looking upon such a birth-place of genius, as this sweet-looking cottage.

A short distance up a rugged narrow lane, named "The Loan on the Hill," off the main road, passing through the quaint little village you come to the humble cottage, now revered as one of the shrines of the country. The village, popularly known as ' Kinnaskit,' rests at the foot of the Lomond Hills, near the northern shore of Loch Leven, and for quiet and varied beauty the scenery, far extending all around, is most charming. There are three other small villages in the neighbourhood. Near Kinnesswood to the west lies Balgedie, where the Rev. Dr. Mackelvie (1800-1863) was long minister of the Secession Church, and took a prominent share in the foundation of the United Presbyterian denomination. He was born at Kinnesswood, and in 1837 produced from personal investigation, one of the best books on the life and works of Michael Bruce. To the east of Kinnesswood there is Portmoak, where the famous Ebenezer Erskine, founder of the Secession Church, was long minister, and in the kirkyard of which both Michael Bruce and his biographer, Dr. Mackelvie, lie buried. A little further east there is Scotlandwell—the *Fons Scotiœ* of old charters—where a hospital was founded by Bishop William Malvoisin of St. Andrew's, previous to 1238, afterwards bestowed on the Red Friars. King Robert the Bruce, on one occasion, drank the water at Scotlandwell, and William Wallace had some daring exploits on the loch. These villages look down upon Loch Leven, in which there is the Isle of St. Serf's, where Andrew Wyntoun, the renowned prior of St. Serf's, wrote his valuable "Orygynale Cronykil of Scotland" about 1406, in the time of James I., and of course there is the Castle Island, the most prominent island on the Loch where Mary Queen of Scots was imprisoned. Thus it may be gathered that the whole district was redolent of romantic and historic memories, as well as of some literary interest, for Sir Walter Scott was a frequent visitor to Blairadam House, which is a very little distance from the south shore of Loch Leven, the whole scene of which is graphically depicted in "The Abbot," one of the most fascinating of Scott's romances. In ancient days the Druids and the Culdees had been settled in the district. All this fitted in with the young poet's fancy, and well he sketched it in his word-pictures of localities still distinguished by those acquainted with the district, which was noted for the manufacture of vellum and parchment from an early period. Many an important legal document has been written upon material prepared in Kinnesswood. It may well be understood why the fireside of Alexander Bruce was so favourite a resort. There was in that home much that was attractive to all parties of varying degrees and ages, and whatever matter was under consideration was always of an interesting character. Poetry was a favourite study, while history afforded a wide field.

Mr. Mackenzie points out that in former days Kinnesswood and the adjoining hamlets, were called the "scattered villages," and were much apart from the world at large. They formed what is even now locally described as "the Bishopshire," which had its principal place there, with lands in feu to the Archbishop of St. Andrew's. The romance of fairyland invests the Lomond Hill, according to local legend, and the denizens of the spirit-world were supposed to hold high festival at various times upon its slopes. Michael Bruce loved his native place, and gives a description of it in the following lines :

> Fair from his hand behold the village rise
> In rural pride, 'mong intermingled trees ;
> Above whose aged tops the joyful swains
> At eventide descending from the hill,
> With eye enamour'd, mark the many wreaths
> Of pillar'd smoke high curling to the clouds,
> How fair a prospect rises to the eye,
> Where Beauty vies in all her vernal forms
> For ever pleasant and for ever new.

The inhabitants were noted for a high degree of intelligence, which is quite evident from their letters and correspondence, and the various mutual improvement societies which existed in the parish did much to give the common life of the people a high tone. "The Pious Memorials of Portmoak," a most interesting unpublished MS. history which had been written by men of the village, is such as any rural parish might be proud of. The people were industrious and happy, and when the day's work was done, the click of the looms and birr of the pirn-wheel had ceased, the young people gathered round the firesides, where the peat fires lent their bright gleams, to listen to the stories of " auld lang syne." These were in ample variety. Yet the "fairy tales" had a charm which entranced the youngsters. They would sit quiet as mice, their eager faces telling how much they enjoyed them, as this relaxation was better suited to their youthful mind than the hard lines and verses of " the Carritch," the name by which the Shorter Catechism was known. Where hills exist there is generally some " weird " story connected with them. So here, Kinnesswood was no exception, for :

> " On Lomond's slopes the warlocks grim,
>   And fairy brownies danced,
> Wae unca tales o' auld lang syne,
>   Held younkers oft entranced."

THE POET'S FATHER

MICHAEL BRUCE'S father, Alexander Bruce, the shrewd weaver, possessed the rare discernment to discover that, at the birth of his fifth child, Michael, the graces had presided ; and in spite of his slender income he indulged the hope that one day he might see him adorning a burgher pulpit. Alexander could boast of little school learning, but he had an inquiring mind. To a large share of common sense he added much reading and more thinking. Poetry, history, and especially theology, were so much his delight, that they often robbed the loom of the attentions due to it. But then he was an adept at the shuttle and could make up for a lengthened diet hour. Like many more who were under the spiritual influence of the celebrated Ebenezer Erskine, Alexander was an exemplary Christian, and he chose for his wife one who to a blithe and lively disposition added all the graces of

KINNISSWOCD
View in the Main Street

From Photo by Mr. Ross, Leslie.

5

true piety. The poet's mother was Ann Bruce, and though of the same name she was not previously related to her husband. Dr. Mackelvie tells us that Ann Bruce was possessed of as much piety as her husband, though not of so much discretion. She was as forward in pronouncing an opinion as he was cautious in forming one, as gay as he was grave. She seemed formed for action, he for contemplation, and accordingly she was the main spring of all the movements in the family. The mother's liveliness, together with the father's reflection, and the piety of both, descended upon Michael, and constituted a character which commanded universal love and esteem. A " Seceder Elder," Auld Saunders was a man of superior intelligence and liberal views, and early threw in his lot with the Secession, being an adherent of the Rev. Thomas Mair of Orwell, who was afterwards ejected from the Anti-Burgher section of the Secession Church for holding the doctrine that there is a sense in which Christ died for all men. Mr. Mair carried the great majority of his congregation with him—about two thousand persons—who elected old Bruce as one of their elders. As each Sabbath came round, the worthy elder and his wife might have been seen wending their way round the loch to the church at Milnathort—a pilgrimage of about nine miles. Those who know what it was to be a " Seceder elder " in those days, will readily believe that, if at all in health old Saunders Bruce appeared at church every Sabbath, fair weather or foul. Bunyan not inaptly says of such an one :

> " Who would true valour see ?
> Let him come thither !
> One here will constant be
> Come wind, come weather ;
> There's no discouragement
> Shall make him once relent
> His first avowed intent
>   To be a pilgrim.'

THE BIRTHPLACE OF MICHAEL BRUCE IN THE LOAN TO THE HILL

If we knew nothing of the forefathers of our Scottish hamlets, but the pure and affectionate songs and ballads, the wild and pathetic airs of music which they loved, we should know enough to convince us that they were a race of men, strong, healthful, and happy, and dignified in the genial spirit of nature. The home where Michael Bruce lived, and moved, and had his being was such as Burns beautifully described in his immortal poem, " The Cottar's Saturday night." The Bible lay from week's end to week's end visible before the eyes of all the inmates of the house, and the language of Scripture was so familiar to the mind, that it was often adopted unconsciously in the conversation of common hours. If Christianity is most beautiful and lovely in the young, the happy, and the innocent, we must yet look for the consummation of its sublimity in those who have well-nigh trod life's path. A family, who, emphatically speaking, fear God, must possess within themselves the elements of all human virtue, happiness, and wisdom—however much these may occasionally be weakened or polluted by the mournful necessities of life—grief, hard labour, penury, and disease. It has even been said that the Scottish peasantry are poetical because they are religious. The study of poetry, in fact, has a tendency to keep men from being worldly-minded. Together with many Christian virtues Alexander Bruce had a rare capacity for social enjoyment. He possessed a huge fund of anecdotes, and in winter nights around the glowing peat hearth, or in summer evenings under the shade of his ash trees, the village youths assembled to hear his stories of the olden time. It is of his father Michael speaks, when he says—

> I knew an aged swain, whose hoary head
> Was bent with years, the village-chronicle,
> Who much had seen, and from the former times
> Much had received. He, hanging o'er the hearth,

In winter evenings, to the gaping swains,
And children circling round the fire, would tell
Stories of old, and tales of other times.
Of Lomond and Levina he would talk ;
And how of old, in Britain's evil days,
When brothers against brothers drew the sword
Of civil rage, the hostile hand of war
Ravaged the land, gave cities to the sword,
And all the country to devouring fire.

THE POET'S FATHER'S FIRESIDE

9

The man who could thus gather the villagers around his hearth must have had a fine vein of humour running through his composition. " A scene," says Dr. Mackelvie, " yet well remembered, was when the father of our poet went down to a bookstall, at one of the fairs in the place, with Michael, then a mere child, in his hand, and inquired for the poems of Sir David Lindsay, the Burns of his day. The vendor of knowledge did not happen to have the book, but on learning that it was intended for the child before him, was so surprised that *he* should wish it, that he took up a little volume entitled, ' A Key to the Gates of Heaven,' and promised to give it to him, on condition that he would read a portion of it upon the spot, which being done to his satisfaction, he awarded him the prize." Dr. Grosart remarks that the little book referred to was probably good old Thomas Brooks' " Privy Key of Heaven," or perchance, Scudder's " Key of Heaven, or the Lord's Prayer Opened."

An account of the venerable elder from the pen of his old apprentice, David Pearson, appeared in the " Missionary Chronicle " for May, 1797. We shall now only give a portion of it, as being of interest at this stage of our narrative. " From his early youth," writes David Pearson, " Alexander Bruce was pious, and filled up his time with duty ; and prudent, so as to know the duty of every time. Daily did he consult the oracles of truth, and, like Apollos, was mighty in the Scriptures. Three years did I dwell with him, and can with truth and sincerity assert that he had an amiable and calm disposition ; a most winning method with young persons, so as to introduce religion to their notice, and recommend its practice by some pleasant narrative, which he was never at a loss to introduce, as he had an extensive acquaintance with the writings of the best historians and divines both ancient and modern. This large stock of information, under the management of that pious disposition which he possessed, was very profitable to me and other youths ; for he was excellent at his business, and taught a number of apprentices, who revered him as a parent, teacher, master, and friend. He was generally very happy in his young men, and they in him. He ruled well his own family and was counted worthy to be chosen an elder to the church, and was a strict adherer to the laws of Christ's house. He had much contentment with his lot, though low, and frequently afflicted. He had much satisfaction in his family, though most of them died young ; the fruits of grace evidenced by his little ones rejoiced his heart ; with gratitude he recorded these things. His oldest child died, aged sixteen months, before he could speak ; but whenever breakfast or supper was over, the child pointed to the shelf where the Bibles lay ; when worship began, he closed his eyes, and laid his hands to his breast, and never made the least movement until service was over. His second child died aged five years and three months ; though young, she interested herself in the welfare of the family : when she became distressed, she told her father she was going to Heaven : on being asked what she would see there she readily answered, " I shall see God in Christ, the holy angels and saints ; and there I shall see your father." About this time there was a poor family in the town, who lost their father : their mother being weak, the children had to beg. He took one of them, a girl of ten years of age. A worthy woman of the place said that God's blessing would rest on his family, for such a kindness. It came to pass, for the girl proved a great help to them, was a kind nurse to his young son Michael, for two years ; and though offered higher fees from greater people in the world, always refused, saying she could not leave her master, for her heart was fastened to him. He was at much pains with the maid, in teaching her the principles of religion. When exhorting her at times, she would weep. He would have said, " Are you angry at me for saying this to you, Mary ? " " O, no ! master," was her reply, " tell me more, say more to me yet ! " After continuing with him four years, she was seized with a fever, which carried her off in 1748. She was well exercised in her trouble ; and told her mistress that she was dying, and would soon be happy. So precious was this poor maid's memory to Alexander, that he paid the expense of her funeral, and named his daughter Mary, out of respect to her. He was not only at pains in teaching his own family, but the children of several poor people came daily to him, whom he taught gratis. The pleasure he took in teaching his son Michael, and seeing his rapid advances after he went to the school and university, was only to be compared with the grief he felt when that extraordinary genius was taken away by death.

Chapter II

BRUCE'S SCHOOLDAYS

As Michael Bruce had learned so much in his infancy from his father it will easily be understood how the baby enthusiasm of little Michael would be kindled, and how eagerly he would desire to know the mysteries of reading, that he might drink at the fountain of learning. We shall now see what an apt and clever pupil he was ; how rapidly he developed in learning, and how he moved among his friends and companions as a boy.

What a feeling of honest pride and satisfaction Alexander Bruce must have felt when he led forth his promising young son, Michael—the pet of the family—to school for the first time. Under the affectionate teaching of his father, Michael was able to read the simple stories of the Bible before he had completed his fourth year, at which age he was sent to the parish school, then only a few doors from his own house, with a Bible for his lesson book.

Mr. Dun, the enthusiastic teacher, was surprised when Michael presented himself with the Bible, at what he considered the stupidity of his parents in sending him to school with the sacred volume instead of the shorter catechism, from which children, then, were invariably taught the art of reading. His surprise, however, Dr. Mackelvie tells us, was transferred from the parents to the child, when upon asking him to shew what he could do, he commenced reading with fluency at the place pointed

13

out to him. At the end of the first week he was considered by his instructor to have been long enough among the easy lessons of the gospels, and was therefore enjoined to bring with him, upon his return, the book read by the more advanced classes. Mr. Dun, in addition to his other requirements, possessed an excellent knowledge of Latin, and was greatly taken with Michael, who held the foremost place in his classes without exciting the jealousy or incurring the envy of his rivals—chief of whom were the schoolmaster's son, and William Arnot the young laird of Portmoak. Michael's pre-eminence was all the more wonderful in that for six successive summers he was tending cattle on the slopes of the Lomonds, and that Arnot and Dun, besides having the advantage of constant attendance, possessed more than average abilities.

In all branches of school learning, Michael made rapid progress, and from a scrap of one of his letters we learn that he could " write " when in his sixth year. " I could write," he says, " or at least scratch my name with the year 1752 below it. In that year I learnt the elements of pencraft ; and now, let me see, 1752 from 1766 leaves fourteen—a goodly term for one to be a scholar." How fortunate was the school master of Portmoak !—the genial page of Virgil darkened with no foreboding frown— besprent with no sullen tears ! How would his countenance brighten up when the gentle boy, with beaming eye and joyous footstep, once more returned to shed the influence of his diligence and genius, after a time of herding, on the studies of the school, and his playful humour on the sport of the playground ! Thus, so far as his school education was concerned, Michael had nothing to complain of except that it was often broken up. But even when keeping his flock he was a diligent student. Herding on the hills, when the shepherd's care is not so much to keep his flock from trespassing, as to prevent its being lost, is to some an unmitigated weariness. To him whose mind

"The Loan to the Hill," Kinnesswood

Bruce's Cottage in the distance, the Schoolroom he attended on the right.

15

lies dormant—who gazes upon earth, water, and sky without discrimination—who has not learned to love reading or interpret nature, what can be more intolerable ? But to one whom the story book absorbs—who finds pleasure in the flower that decks the field, or in the callow brood that nestles in the brake—whose ear alternately delights in the singing of the birds, the whimpling of brooks, the stir of the gentle breeze among the trees, or the rolling storms—for whom every cairn has its legend, and every ruin its history—these solitudes are invested with many charms. Nor can we forget that, in spite of the disadvantages of self-teaching in such retirement, some of the finest geniuses have been matured.

Who will regret that John Brown, of Haddington, spent his early days on the braes of Abernethy, learning Latin and Greek, and studying his Bible ? Or what philosopher laments the humble circumstances which compelled James Ferguson to betake himself to the hills of Banff, where time and cattle and food, too, were often forgotten among his books, wheels and globes ? Among the hills it was that the enthusiasm was nursed, the habits of perseverance acquired, which fitted the one for being an explorer in the field of theology, and the other in the science of astronomy.

Referring to the period of six successive summers when Michael Bruce was a shepherd lad, Dr. Mackelvie finely remarks that " although deprived during this period of the benefits of a living instructor, his mind was schooling itself in the elements of poetry, by imbibing those impressions which Nature, when she presents her-self in the sublime and beautiful, never fails to make upon susceptible minds. Cowper affirms that ' the love of nature's works is born with all.' But few appear to possess an exquisite relish for its beauties. Michael Bruce, however, child as he was, even then ' looked round on nature and on life with the eye which nature bestows only on a poet.' The impressions which he imbibed thus early remained with him, and were the same upon which he fell back, when in after life he was shut out from the society of kindred spirits, and deprived of such scenery as his eye could rest upon with delight. He then placed himself in imagination upon the knoll on which he had often reclined when tending his herd, and lived over again those delicious moments when life was new, and when nature, for the first time, presented to him some of her loveliest scenes. His poem on ' Lochleven ' is wholly made up of these reminiscences, and ought to be regarded by the reader as the impressions of the shepherd boy clothed in the language of the student and the scholar. This capability of communing with Nature kept him as cheerful, though alone, as the urchin who had neglected his charge to join his fellow cowherds in their childish sports.

"For all those whom chance threw in his way in this solitude he had his little joke ready ; and if he found them intelligent and communicative, he would get them to sit down beside him, and tarry till he examined them on all they knew. The proprietor of Upper Kinneston, a small estate upon the south-west declivity of the Lomond Hills, related with much feeling the amusing stories told him and the strange questions put to him by Michael when herding his father's cattle, and how he would offer his services to carry the boy's meals to the hill for the sake of having half-an-hour's conversation with this interesting youth."

We do not regret, therefore, that our poet's humble lot made him a shepherd boy. Steeped in the lore of his native hills, his pockets stuffed with the most popular ballads of the day, and furnished, as years advanced, with the best English authors, being withal an ardent admirer of nature, we need not wonder that he never sings more sweetly than when his native hills and dales are his theme.

17

C

How fair a prospect rises to the eye,
Where beauty vies in all her vernal forms,
For ever pleasant, and for ever new !
Swells the exulting thought, expands the soul,
Drowns each ruder care : a blooming train
Of bright ideas rushes on the mind.
Imagination rouses at the scene,
And backward, thro' the gloom of ages past,
Beholds Arcadia, like a rural Queen,
Encircled with her swains and rosy nymphs,
The mazy dance conducting on the green.

From the very first of his school days in Kinnesswood, Michael Bruce displayed remarkable intelligence and ability for learning, which made him at once the prodigy of the village school, and was destined to carry him almost at a single bound into the front rank of poetic genius.

While yet a mere boy Michael acquired a power of utterance in prayer that was quite marvellous, early discovering that the secret of the Lord is with them that fear and love Him. To him Jesus was a living, bright, and personal reality. In Christ he found the peace with God, the love, the life, the lasting joy, the rest and satisfaction to his soul that true believers have ever found in all ages. It was a true expression of this feeling when he sang—

O, happy is the man who hears
Instruction's warning voice,
And who celestial Wisdom makes
His early only choice.

The day-dreams of conversion, which we hear of on every side, are the types of substantial realities. Of this all who are familiar with the lives of M'Cheyne, Wilberforce, Garfield, and many other noble characters will be convinced. Mrs. Garfield was a most exemplary mother and a woman of great faith. When her son James, President of America, was perplexed as to what he should become when he was a young man, his mother pressed upon him, first the importance of giving himself to Christ, and then waiting for guidance. The advice was taken, and we all know with what satisfactory results. Dr. George Macdonald, the famous author, addressing some school-boys on one occasion, said that he might be expected to give them some advice on their future careers when they left school, but it did not matter much what career they followed so long as they had Jesus Christ for their leader and followed Him, and in the end they would meet with success and have their reward.

Dr. Mackelvie tells us that Bruce's conversation was very generally about sacred things ; and the enjoyment he felt when any new thought connected with theology was suggested to him, was rendered obvious by his again reverting to the topic after it had been dropped. When at any time his father was from home at the usual hour for family prayer, Michael, by the common consent of the household, led the devotions. It was stated to his biographer, by a person who was once present upon an occasion of this kind, and was, besides, well qualified to judge of what was becoming in such circumstances, that he was impressed with a sense of incongruity in a child acting as the domestic minister in a family where there were at the time both a man and a matron ; but that, before the boy had concluded the service, he was so struck with the propriety of his language, the variety of scriptural allusions, the suitableness of the petitions, and the solemnity of the manner, that he could hardly permit himself to believe that the boy whom he saw uttered the prayer which he heard. To this devotional feeling he gave expression in a number of beautiful Gospel sonnets to which we will give attention further on. His very life was the expression of piety and cheerfulness. All who were his associates at school agreed in ascribing an unaccountable " weight " and influence to all he said and did. It was a common saying that Michael's word was of as great authority as the master's. His look was a reproach to the quarrelsome; his help and sympathy were extended to the injured, and all disputes were settled by him. It is unspeakably touching to find the loving way in which William Arnot, David Pearson, John Birrel, and others of his schoolmates, in long after years, spoke of him. At home the same indefinable deference was paid to him, and he is described by his biographer, whom we have already quoted, as *a pet*, but not a spoiled child. As very rarely happens, he appears to have been the Joseph of the family, without provoking the envy of his brethren.

All the children of Mr. and Mrs. Bruce were removed by death, at a comparatively early age, except two, a son and daughter. James, the last member of the family, who received most of his education at home from his father, was very much attached to Michael. He was possessed of good common sense which enabled him to take his place among those who had been better educated. Persons of a prosaic turn of mind may question whether common sense and poetry can be combined, but these qualities at least entered into the composition of James Bruce. He frequently strung verses together with great facility to the amusement of the villagers, who never hesitated to furnish him with subjects. His verses were written after the manner of Ramsay and Fergusson, and one poem entitled " The Farmer," consisting of about fifty stanzas, was printed, being valued more, it is supposed, for its wholesome advice than its poetry. We quote only one verse here to give the reader an idea of the style of verse :—

> These days are gane ! oh ! weel I ween
> No sixty-five times I hae seen
> Spring robe the Lomond Hill wi' green,
>   Awa I'm wearin',
> But still to farmer lads a keen
>   True love I'm bearin'.

Both Dr. Mackelvie and Dr. Grosart apply the description of Beattie's Minstrel to Michael Bruce, although it is not likely that his existence was known to that bard, and we may be excused for making use of the same passage now :—

> . . . " Poor Edwin was no vulgar boy,
> Deep thought oft seemed to fix his infant eye ;
> Dainties he heeded not, nor gaud, nor toy,
> Save one short pipe of rudest minstrelsy.
>
> Silent when glad, affectionate though shy,
> And now his look was most demurely sad,
> And now he laughed aloud, yet none knew why ;
> And neighbours stared, and sighed, and blessed the lad ;
> Some deem'd him wondrous wise, and some believed him mad."

Chapter III

HIS SCHOOL COMPANIONS

A youth of poetical tastes, elevated and refined by such piety, can be the bosom friend of few ; and it is worthy of note that those who associated with Michael in his boyhood were inspired with kindred enthusiasm, and pervaded with the same deep religious feeling. We would refer first to David Pearson, who was apprentice to Bruce's father, and continued some time to work with him as journeyman, sleeping in the house with Michael as his bedfellow. He was a year older than the poet, and is justly described by Dr. Anderson, in his life of Bruce, as " a man of strong parts, and a serious, contemplative, and inquisitive turn who had improved his mind by a diligent and solitary perusal of such books as came within his reach." He had a natural taste for poetry which he and young Bruce stimulated in one another, and they often wrote upon the same subjects. After leaving home Bruce kept up a correspondence with Pearson, being in the habit of submitting his poems to him till within a few weeks of his death. This person was, therefore, in an excellent position to give evidence as to what the poet wrote when such evidence was needed.

John Birrell, another of Bruce's companions, received a somewhat liberal education. Although he was considerably younger than Bruce and Pearson, he was very early in life admitted into the intimacy of both, and afterwards became

22

the elder Bruce's most intimate friend. Mr. Birrel contributed in prose and verse to the " Edinburgh Magazine," " Perth Magazine," the " Christian Repository," and other periodicals, being regarded as a man of sound judgment and undoubted piety. Bruce was fortunate and happy in the companions of his schooldays. Their literary tastes are fully attested by the essays and verses which they composed for their mutual cultivation, and which are still preserved ; whilst their blameless lives and happy deaths prove that their religion was " no chimera, but something real." It was in the society of these genial spirits that his muse gave its early utterances ; and we cannot doubt that the poet was largely benefited by their generous praise and kindly criticism.

PREPARING FOR COLLEGE

Michael, following the bent of his mind, and gratifying a long cherished wish of his father, decided to study for the ministry, and at the age of eleven joined a class of senior pupils in order to " prepare " for college. Along with the children of " portioners " in the parish, and a son of the village teacher, Mr. Dun, who was an excellent classic, Michael soon acquired a knowledge of Latin, which came to him, it was said, as had his mother tongue. He was always dux, and one of his most intimate friends in the class was William Arnot, son of Mr. David Arnot, proprietor of Portmoak. From Dr. Mackelvie we learn that " William Arnot was a boy of lively parts, studious habits, and warm heart. In addition to a liberal education at school, he enjoyed at home the instructions of a father, who combined a highly improved taste with great intelligence and piety. Reared amidst scenery calculated to inspire the mind with poetic sentiment, and associated from his earliest years with youths who had been favoured by the muse, he could hardly fail to be operated upon by such influence, and to become intelligent, poetic, and pious. This congeniality of sentiment and feeling, which characterized Bruce and Arnot, led them to cherish each other with even more than fraternal fondness, and, accordingly, rendered them inseparable companions. This friendship, so pure and warm, was suddenly and prematurely broken up by the death of Arnot, while yet a boy at school. This breach gave the first of many shocks to Bruce's feelings, which, during his brief career on earth, he received, and which threw over his natural cheerfulness a tinge of sadness. Visiting the spot, some four years after, where this most intimate companion of his boyhood is interred, he wrote a monody to his memory, and enclosed it in the following letter to Arnot's father :—

" Gairney Bridge, May 29, 1765.

Walking lately by the churchyard of your town, which inspires a kind of veneration for our ancestors, I was struck with these beautiful lines of Mr. Gray, in his ' Elegy written in a country churchyard,'

> ' Perhaps, in this neglected spot is laid,
> Some heart once pregnant with celestial fire,'

and immediately I called to mind your son, whose memory will be ever dear unto me ; and, with respect to that place, put the supposition out of doubt. I wrote the most part of this poem the same day, which I should be very sorry if you look upon as a piece of flattery : I know you are above flattery, and if I know my own mind, I am so, too. It is the language of the heart ; I think a lie in verse and prose the same. The versification is irregular, in imitation of Milton's Lycidas."

24

The manner in which Bruce speaks of his friend, a boy of fifteen, will appear to our readers like flattery, when they find him writing thus of him :—

> " Oft by the side of Leven's crystal lake,
> Trembling beneath the closing lids of light,
> With slow, short-measured steps, we took our walk ;
> Then he would talk
> Of argument far, far-above his years ;
> Then he would reason high,
> Till from the east, the silver queen of night
> Her journey up heaven's steep began to make,
> And silence reigned attentive in the sky."

But it is considered by all who knew Arnot, that Bruce has not overrated him, for he was a youth of great attainments, considering his years, and gave promise of pre-eminence in whatever profession he might have chosen. It is believed that our poet's early companionship with this youth was useful to him ever afterwards, by stimulating him to the greatest efforts of which he was capable, from seeing in his friend what effort could accomplish.

Such was the happy company of youths whose intelligence and piety shed additional lustre on a parish already famous as the residence, if not the birth-place of Andrew Wyntoun, and the scene of Ebenezer Erskine's labours. The death of William Arnot was a severe blow to Michael, but it had the effect of drawing him into closer intimacy and sympathy with Mr. Arnot, who encouraged him to frequent his house, till he might be said to be a member of the family. Mr. Arnot recognised and appreciated Bruce's talents, and to him the poet was indebted for his first introduction to Shakespeare, Pope, Young, and other distinguished names. This kind patron, who acted like a father towards Michael, was a man of fine character, rare sagacity, good judgment, and considerable culture.

Bruce himself gives us the following portrait of his friend :

> " Learned but not fraught
> With self-importance, as the starched fool
> Who challenges respect by solemn face—
> By studious accent, and high sounding phrase,
> Enamoured of the shade, but not morose—
> Politeness raised in courts, by frigid rule,
> With him spontaneous grows. Not books alone,
> But man, his study, and the better part
> To tread the ways of virtue, and to act
> The various scenes of life with God's applause.
> Deep in the bottom of the flowery vale
> With blooming sallows, and the twine
> Of verdant alders fenced, his dwelling stands
> Complete in rural elegance. The door,
> By which the poor, or pilgrim never passed,
> Still open, speaks the master's bounteous heart."

After the death of his son, Mr. Arnot seems to have regarded Michael, who had free access to his well-filled library, as his own child, and his letters ever afterward were more those of a parent than a patron. To the end they corresponded, and many an unostentatious present witnessed to the thoughtfulness and tenderness of this gentleman's regard. Like all circles the class, to which Michael Bruce belonged, was soon broken up. Young Dun went to college, and Willie Arnot, as we have seen,

> Crept like a rose before 'tis fully blown,
> Or fully half disclosed,

had joined the happy throng above. Bruce, at this time fifteen years of age, began seriously to think of what university he should attend. " His intention," Dr. Grosart says, " was to offer himself as a candidate for a bursary or scholarship in St. Andrews ; but a companion of his own having been excluded from the competition, Bruce, suspecting that his connection with the Secession Church had operated against him, resolved, rather than hazard rejection, not to apply. His thoughts were next directed to Edinburgh. In the interval he employed himself at leisure hours in transcribing large portions of Milton and of Thomson ; and he was ' imping his wing for larger flight ' than he had yet indulged.

" While he was still somewhat uncertain as to the future after leaving the village school, a letter came to his father, informing him that a relative had died, and bequeathed him 2oo merks Scots (£11, 2s. 2d.). It was received as a direct ' gift ' from God. It was at once separated to Michael's use, and he proceeded to enrol himself as a student in the University of Edinburgh. His unfailing friend, Mr. Arnot of Portmoak, declared his readiness to render what assistance lay in his power ; and the monthly ' chest,' as it passed from Kinnesswood to Edinburgh, showed that he did not fail of his promise ; for there went in it now a little ' kit ' of sweet butter, and now a dozen new-laid eggs, even well-nigh all the presents to David at Mahanaim—' honey, and butter, and sheep, and cheese of kine ' (2 Sam. xvii. 29)."

Bruce soon entered the university, leaving behind him a favourable impression in the village. So highly were his poems thought of that the villagers procured copies of them, and committed them to memory. Thus it was that, from some of those who long survived Bruce and his father, Dr. Anderson, and at a later date Dr. Mackelvie, learned many of the facts regarding Bruce himself and his poetry which they have related.

Bruce's cottage was a resort of the more intelligent young men in the district who delighted to drop in of an evening and listen to Alexander Bruce, the father, discussing various topics, about which they wanted information. Michael Bruce formed a literary society among

27

these young men, of which his father, Alexander Bruce, was also a member, and it was their practice for each member to write an essay under a nom-de-plume. The one by which Alexander Bruce was known was ' Acastro,' and Mr. John Birrell by that of ' Varo.' It may be helpful if we give a key to the pseudonyms for Bruce's friends, as the reader will occasionally find in Bruce's poems reference to these friends under their noms-de-plume. The following is a list of these names as far as we have been able to discover :

" Philinor "	David Pearson
" Lycidas "	John Pearson
" Varo "	John Birrell
" Amyentor "	Ralph Birrell
" Theandor "	John Bennet
" Damon "	James Bruce
" Aspasio "	Andrew Small
" Amyntas "	Michael Bruce
" Acastro "	Alexander Bruce
" Philo "	James Campbell
" Agricola "	Dr. Arnot of Portmoak
" Philander "	Henry Arnot, Kinnesswood
" Philoclis "	William Dryburgh
" Daphnis "	William Arnot
" Laelius "	George Henderson

Token of Mr. Eben. Erskine
of Stirling.

Token of Mr. Alexr. Moncrieff,
Abernethy.

Chapter IV

BRUCE AT THE UNIVERSITY

In due course Bruce entered the University of Edinburgh, where his distinguished talents and engaging manners procured him many friends, chief of whom were Mr. George Henderson of Turfhills, afterwards the Rev. George Henderson, of what is now the United Presbyterian congregation, " Greyfriars," Glasgow ; Mr. David Greig, afterwards minister of Lochgelly ; Mr. George Lawson, afterwards Professor Lawson of Selkirk ; William Dryborough of Dysart, who died in his eighteenth year ; and John Logan, who has been described as the Judas of the band. Very little has been left on record of Bruce's progress and position in the University, but his fellow students, Henderson, Greig, and Lawson were wont in after years to speak of him and his many attributes with enthusiasm. Dr. Anderson thus briefly sums up his course :—" He applied himself to several branches of literature and philosophy with remarkable assiduity and success. Of the Latin and Greek languages he acquired a masterly knowledge ; and he made eminent progress in Metaphysics, Mathematics, and Moral and Natural Philosophy. But the Belles Lettres was his favourite pursuit, and poetry his darling study." Bruce became a member of a literary society that met once a week during the college session. According to the rules of the society each member was expected to read an essay in turn to the meeting. Michael Bruce, on his turn, preferred verse to prose, and read a poem on " The Last Day," which was much admired by some members of the society, but many critics deemed that Bruce had not been successful in this piece. This will be the general opinion of all who have read it, but to expect that Bruce at such an early age should be successful in a subject which would demand all the resources of a mind like Milton's, was to expect an impossibility according to Dr. Johnson, who remarks in his life of Philips, that " he began to meditate a poem on the Last Day, a subject on which no mind can hope to equal expectation." Knowing that Bruce was possessed with the " faculty divine," he was often asked by several of his fellow-students to furnish them with verses in commendation of their friends or censure on their rivals. To such requests he invariably turned a deaf ear, although his mind was more inclined to be in a sportive than a serious mood, but the tenderness that dwelt in his nature would not allow him to hurt the feelings of others, and he chose rather to sacrifice his reputation for talent than lose the satisfaction arising from " a conscience void of offence." Thus on one ocasion he wrote his friend Arnot :—" I was about to entertain you with a character not altogether unknown to you, of a talker, or story teller, but I do not choose merely for a little diversion, to incur the reprehension of any person living." On one occasion, however, Bruce was induced to apply a little gentle satire to a conceited youth belonging to the literary society, to which we have referred. This aspiring youth boasted that he could write a style superior to Addison, or any popular author of the day, and when his turn came to read an essay, at the suggestion of the members, Bruce produced for the young man's benefit the "Fable of the Eagle, Crow and Shepherd," in which, as the moral of the tale, he tendered this piece of

wholesome advice to the inflated would-be-understood
great man :—

> " My son, said he, warned by this wretch,
> Attempt no deed above your reach ;—
> An eagle not an hour ago—
> He's now content to be a crow."

Shortly after entering the University, and on being
apprized that his brother James had become a weaver,
Michael addressed to him a poem entitled "Weaving Spirit-
ualized." We give the last two verses of this poem, not
for any merit they possess, but as showing the piety of
Bruce, who was at that time in his sixteenth year :—

> Thine eye the web runs keenly o'er
> For things amiss, unseen before—
> Thus scan thy life—mend what's amiss—
> Next day correct the faults of this.

> For when the web is at an end,
> 'Tis then too late a fault to mend—
> Let thought of this awaken dread—
> Repentance dwells not with the dead.

Michael was a young man of refined tastes, and had a
great love for books, being anxious always to secure
the best editions of such books as his heart was set upon.
His means were limited, however, and in this connection
we find him writing to Mr. Arnot, on November 27, 1764 :
" I daily meet with proofs that money is a necessary
evil. When in an auction, I often say to myself, how happy
should I be if I had money to purchase such a book !
How well should my library be furnished ! ' Nisi obstat
res angusta domi.' "

> ' My lot forbids, nor circumscribes alone
> My growing virtues, but my crimes confine."

He proceeds : " Whether any virtues would have accompanied me in a more elevated station, is uncertain ; but that a number of vices, of which my sphere is incapable, would have been its attendants, is unquestionable. The Supreme Wisdom has seen this meet, and the Supreme Wisdom cannot err." The books which Michael Bruce bequeathed to his friends were beautiful copies of the finest editions. There can be no doubt he was in straitened circumstances while prosecuting his studies at the University, but it is gratifying to know that kindly assistance was rendered to him by his father, Mr. Arnot of Portmoak, and other kind friends. Like many other students then as now, at the close of each session of College, Bruce had to look out for employment towards augmenting his funds and meeting the demands of another winter. In the earlier summers he resided chiefly with Mr. Arnot, and Mr. White of Pittendreich, constantly wooing the Muses in spite of depression of spirits and headache. Many of his productions were written during these summer months of vacation.

It is not easy to say precisely when Michael Bruce began to write poetry, as he does not give any dates in the important quarto volume, into which he copied most of his poems. The origin of his paraphrases of scripture subjects, however, can be definitely fixed. Fuller details will be given in considering the paraphrases further on in this volume, but we know that in 1764 Michael Bruce attended a singing class conducted by Mr. John Buchan for training the younger members in Church psalmody. At that time it was reckoned almost a sin to use the metrical version of the psalms for the purpose of practice, and accordingly some nonsensical doggerel rhymes were substituted, and at Buchan's request Michael Bruce wrote a number of sacred hymns as a substitute. It is asserted that thirteen or more of these improved substitutes were abridged and used in the paraphrases, which appear in the Scottish Bibles.

When Bruce was home on a visit during the Christmas holidays of his last session at College, a proposal was made to him by some of the inhabitants of Gairney Bridge, a small hamlet about two miles south of Kinross, to open a school there. Writing from Edinburgh to Mr. Arnot, respecting this proposal, he says :—" I am in great concern just now for a school. When I was over last, there was a proposal made by some people of these parts to keep one at Gairney Bridge. How it may turn out I cannot tell." Bruce wrote a letter to another friend about the same time that he wrote the above to Mr. Arnot. We get a glimpse in it of how the Portmoak people performed their sepulchral rites in those days. We shall allow Bruce to speak without any comment : —" Last week I made a visit to Portmoak, the parish where I was born, and being accidentally at the funeral of an aged rustic, I was invited to partake of the usual entertainment before the interment. We were conducted into a barn, and placed almost in a square,

> When lo ! a mortal, bulky, grave and dull,
> The mighty master of the sevenfold skull,
> Arose like Ajax. In the midst he stands—
> A well filled bicker loads his trembling hands.
> To one he comes, assumes a visage new—
> ' Come ask a blessing, John ?—'tis put on you.'
> ' Bid Mungo say,' says John, with half a face,
> Famed for his length of beard and length of grace.
> Thus have I seen, beneath a hollow rock,
> A shepherd hunt his dogs among his flock—
> ' Run collie, Battie, Venture ' Not one hears,
> Then rising, runs himself, and running swears.

In short, Sir, as I have not time to poetize, the grace is said, the drink goes round, the tobacco pipes are lighted and from a cloud of smoke a hoary-headed rustic addressed the company thus :—' Weel John (*i.e.* the deceased), noo when he's gone was a good, sensible man, stout, and healthy, and hail ; and had the best hand for casting peats of onybody in this kintra side. A weel, Sirs, we maun a' dee—Here's to ye.' I was struck with the speech of this honest man, especially with his heroic application of the glass, in dispelling the gloomy thoughts of death."

Bruce was regarded as a successful and diligent student, and when he left the University the highest expectations were formed of him.

Chapter V

THE YOUNG SCHOOLMASTER

After leaving College, the poet commenced teaching at Gairney Bridge, and here he began " to tune the rural pipe to love." The village is memorable in the history of the Secession Church, being the place where Ebenezer Erskine and his three fellow seceders constituted themselves into a separate communion. On 6th December, 1883, the anniversary of the formation of the first Secession Presbytery, the foundation stone of the monument that now stands at Gairney Bridge as a memorial to the Secession fathers, was laid with all due honour. Fifteen years previous to Bruce's incumbency the school had, for a short time, been taught by John Brown—afterwards the celebrated Dr. Brown of Haddington—under whose vigorous mind and effective hand it acquired local fame, and attracted pupils from great distances. We have interesting glimpses of Bruce while engaged at this school, and here is an episode of his life with Dr. Mackelvie's remarks :—" The school was kept in an old cottage which happened to be previously untenanted. A few deals laid on blocks of wood sufficed for forms, and an old table served as writing desk. This latter article of furniture was so frail, that before the first month transpired, in which it had been so used, it was damaged beyond repair. Upon this disaster the poet addressed the following letter (facsimile appears in frontispiece), to Mr. Flockhart, proprietor of the lands of Annafrech, who took the active management of the school :—

'Sir,—The following will inform you that we are in a *tableless* condition (if you will excuse the novelty of the word), which I desire you to take into consideration. I was about to say a great many fine things on the subject, but I find they are all slipt out of my head. To your wife and brother make the compliments of—

Yours sincerely,

Michael Bruce.' "

Accompanying the letter was a poem on " The Fall of the Table," see the poems.

Bruce had a very different experience at Gairney Bridge from his predecessor, Dr. John Brown. We cannot but regret that his gentle nature and delicate frame had ever to grapple with the work of a school. Not that he was unqualified for teaching, nor that he did not find pleasure in it ; but his aversion to anything like effective corporal punishment, which is always more or less necessary, almost emptied the school which his learning, piety, and humour, if these had been backed by the firmness of the predecessor just named, would in ordinary circumstances have kept full. With all deference to those who would entirely banish the rod, those pupils are the happiest, the most diligent, the most respectful, who are at once under the gentle offices of love and the practical expression of her sterner dictates ; and, however much we may sympathise with the exuberance of persuasive power in which our young teacher placed his confidence, we cannot but admire the sound sense of his friends, Arnot and Dryburgh, who wrote to him when he entered upon his school duties, as follows:—" The energies of the young," said Mr. Arnot, " will be sure to lie dormant, if they be

THE SECESSION MEMORIAL AT GAIRNEY BRIDGE
Foundation Stone laid by Rev. Principal John Cairns, D.D., LL.D.,
on third jubilee day, 6th December, 1883.

not roused by those to whom their training is entrusted, as most soils are barren without cultivation. But there is much need of prudence, for, as some ground requires the stronger plough, another plot may be managed by an easy hand. With some force must be used—forbearance must be employed towards others. You have the advantage of spurring them up by emulation, which seldom fails but which, at the same time, does not always succeed. *By this common impulse I could not be affected."*

Mr. Dryburgh said :—" Now that you have taken up a school, I beg to remind you that you are a pedagogue— neither be too gentle nor too severe The one treatment is as bad as the other, but if there be any difference, I think indulgence the worse of the two. But, on the other hand, there are many who, professing to whip blockheads, ought to undergo a similar punishment for being one themselves—to whom the words of Solomon, which Dean Swift once chose for his text, may be very well applied, ' Stripes are for the back of fools .' " But these advices, however kindly taken, were all in vain ; and their attempt to harden up the young sentimentalist was all the more abortive in that it was then he fell under the most softening of all powers—a power to which the sternest natures have yielded ; the stoutest hearts given way ; and we appeal to those striplings in the profession who may have lately come within range of Cupid's shafts, whether in such a wounded condition their arm has not lost a little of its power.

We do not wonder then that it was an easy time for the youngsters of Gairney Bridge, when the charms of Magdalene Grieve, daughter of his kindly host, stole softly o'er the poet's heart. At Gairney Bridge, Bruce's emoluments did not exceed £11 a year, and among his poems in this volume will be found a satirical dialogue on the subject of school fees (see page 73).

In addition to the school fees, and in place of salary,

it was agreed that Bruce should reside and receive free
board with the wealthier parents of the children who
attended school. Accordingly he went to Classlochie,
a farm then possessed by a Mr. Grieve—a man of excellent
Christian character, who was so " taken " by his guest
that he would not hear of his leaving him to go elsewhere
during the whole period he taught at Gairney Bridge.
" All round about," Dr. Grosart remarks, " were good
neighbours ;   and every farmer's ingle gave hospitable
welcome to the shy, gentle student-teacher. Tradition
garners memories of visits at the Brackleys, and Cavil-
stone, Annafrech, and Turfhills. In each of these farms
were to be found fine specimens of the old type of
Scottish laird ;   some naturally wild, perchance, but
subdued and well-nigh reverential in the presence of
Michael." But for reasons at which we have already
hinted, that was indeed

A HAPPY TIME

for the poet and lover. Mr. Grieve had a daughter,
Magdalene, to whom the poet became most warmly
attached. She was a year younger than Michael, and
afterwards became the wife of Mr. David Low, proprietor
of Cleish Mill and Wester Cleish. Dr. Mackelvie des-
scribes her as " a young woman of modest appearance
and agreeable manners, with a large portion of natural
good-sense. The poet's fancy, however, decked her out
with fascinations sufficiently numerous and striking ;
and had she been as he describes her, she must not only
have been his, but every other person's favourite who
saw her."

> In the flower of her youth, in the bloom of eighteen,
> Of virtue the goddess, of beauty the queen :
> One hour in her presence an era excels
> Amid courts, where ambition with misery dwells.

When in beauty she moves by the brook of the plain
You would call her a Venus new sprung from the main :
When she sings, and the woods with their echoes reply,
You would think that an angel was warbling on high.

Besides the " Pastoral Song," from which these verses are quoted, our poet has celebrated this lady by the name of "Eumelia" and " Peggy " in his " Lochleven," "Alexis" and " Lochleven no More." His humour never sported more playfully ; his fancy never revelled more wildly in the fond exaggeration of love ; and yet after all it is probable that, like Cowper, he was too modest to declare himself and taste what the author of the " Grave " calls the " unappropriated sweets." Magdalene understood and felt the warm feeling with which Bruce regarded her, knowing this instinctively, no doubt, as all true lovers do in a way which no language can express. She was wont to speak of Bruce with touching affection, but always declared that he had never " asked " her. Excessive modesty, and a presentiment that his days were numbered, have been assigned as reasons for his leaving unspoken a love that seems to have been burning in its shy passionateness, and enduring to the end of his brief life. Dr. Grosart informs us that a stanza, by a well-known character, communicated to him by Mr. David Marshall, Kinross, intended to immortalize this love-story, is still in circulation in the county. It is as follows :

In Cleish Kirk-yard lies Magdalene Grieve,
A lass (sweetheart) o' Bruce the poet ;
And Tammie Walker made this verse,
To let the world know it.

In his poem of " Lochleven " when referring to his residence in Gairney Bridge, Bruce says—-

First on thy banks the Doric reed I tuned.

THE COTTAGE AT GAIRNEY BRIDGE

In which the Secession Fathers met, 6th December, 1733, and where John Brown, afterwards Professor at Haddington, taught a school, followed by Michael Bruce in 1765.

Gairney Bridge was evidently, therefore, the birth-place of his love verses, as by " the Doric reed," we presume he means these. But the time soon came when Gairney's banks and the sweet shores of Lochleven must disappear from his sight. Sorest pang of all : he must leave Eumelia, but still she occupies the chief place in his affections. It is well-known, however, that Bruce continued his attachment to Magdalene till death, and sang of her after he had left her father's house in strains which, though somewhat sad, are often the sweetest :—

> But wherever I wander, by night or by day,
> True love to my Peggy still with me shall stay ;
> And ever and aye my loss I'll deplore,
> Till the woodlands re-echo Lochleven no more.
>
> But if Fate has decreed that it ne'er shall be so,
> Then grief shall attend me wherever I go ;
> Till from life's stormy sea I reach death's silent shore,
> Then I'll think upon her and Lochleven no more.

Now it appears, according to Mr. Mackenzie, with whom I fully agree, that Dr. Mackelvie and other biographers, such as the Rev. Wm. Stephen and Dr. Grosart, were wrong in identifying the object of the poet's love with Magdalene Grieve. With reference to this love episode in a conversation I had with Mr. Mackenzie on one occasion, I observed in a good-humoured way that at such a distance of time it did not much matter to whom the poet referred, as there were still many Peggys in the district who had all the charms set out by the poet, and any of them could apply the description to themselves. " Whoever communicated this story to Dr. Mackelvie," writes Mr. Mackenzie, "must have had little acquaintance with the facts of the case, for a careful investigation of the statements in question completely disproves the allegation, as the circumstances cited will not accord with the known facts regarding it. The young woman's name is given as Magdalene, and the addendum is also supplied that she afterwards became the wife of David Low, proprietor of Cleish Mill and Wester Cleish. Evidence is also supposed to be furnished by one of Bruce's poems as follows :—

In the flower of her youth, in the bloom of eighteen, etc.

Also in the poem, " Lochleven no More," it is stated :

Farewell to Loch Leven and Gairney's fair shore,
How sweet on its banks of my Peggy to dream, etc.

We find there is a headstone in Cleish Churchyard, on which the following is recorded :—

Sacred to the memory of *Alexander* Low, late of Dowhill Mill, who died 29th December, 1809, aged 69 years. Also his spouse, " Margery Grieve," who died 17th February 1817, aged 65 years.

This shows that in 1765 she was *not* in the bloom of eighteen but was completing her twelfth year. Rather young for such a love romance ! To the mind of so gentle and kindly a nature as Bruce, only friendship would have a place there. But the facts are as follows :—that the husband of Magdalene Grieve was named Alexander, not David ; that he was not of Cleish Mill, but of ' Dowhill Mill ' ; that he was no proprietor, but simply tenant of this mill. Nor was it likely that the poet would sit on the banks of the Gairney dreaming of a maiden possessing the name of Peggy, eighteen years of age, if he were actually residing in the house with the same, and if she were one of his pupils. A search in the old register books of Portmoak shows that there was a portioner named White who resided in Portmoak. He had a daughter named Margaret, who would be exactly in her eighteenth year when the poet wrote the above, while the common term for Margaret is Peggy. What could have been more natural than that while absent, and with Lochleven water between them, he viewed with romantic interest the home of this girl and the braes where they had often played together in former days ? Here, we believe, is a true solution of the love story. Other poems of Bruce also confirm this theory."

In a letter we had from Mr. David Marshall in 1886, referring to the relationship of Bruce's family to Mr. White, proprietor of Pittendreich, we have further confirmation that it was no doubt Mr. White's daughter who was the object of the young poet's affections. Anyhow, Michael Bruce was not one of those poets who, by dint of imagination, have written of the female sex with a fervour which they never felt. Peggy was a real character, and not a creature of the imagination.

While at Gairney Bridge the poet contemplated the publication of a volume of " Poems," but could not command courage to appear in the character of an author, notwithstanding the entreaties of his friends who were confident of his success. As his connection with Gairney Bridge had ceased, and his literary course at College was finished, he now began to think of entering upon the study of divinity.

Chapter VI

ENTERING THE "THEOLOGICAL HALL"

What is the pomp of learning ? the parade
Of letters and of tongues ? E'en as the mists
Of the gray morn before the rising sun,
That pass away and perish.

Michael Bruce had arrived at that stage in his
curriculum of study at which students with his aspirations generally enter the " Theological Hall," and we
now regard him as a student of Divinity. Before leaving
College he was induced to apply for admission to the Moral
Philosophy class of the Anti-Burgher Synod at Alloa,
but there were theological obstacles in the way. The
synod required that candidates for admission to their
philosophical class should be either members or regular
hearers in their body, and Bruce supposed himself belonging to this latter class ; but the presbytery to which he
applied thought otherwise, and therefore decided that
his application be not then received, but that he be
encouraged to renew it at some future period. To this
decision they probably came in the expectation that,
before he renewed his application, he would withdraw
from the ministry of Mr. Mair, and connect himself with
some of the congregations under the inspection of the
synod. It is a pity the Church at that time had not been
animated by a more liberal and tolerant spirit. Michael

Bruce had hoped to support himself by teaching a school in Alloa or its neighbourhood, being exempt, as all students attending the Hall were, from the payment of class fees, and the decision of the synod was a severe disappointment to him. Naturally he turned to the Burghers, or Associate Synod, with whose attitude toward what was called the " Burgess Oath " he sympathized, rather than with the narrower "Antis." He was accordingly admitted to the fellowship of the Church by the Rev. John Swanston of Kinross, who had been appointed Professor of Theology by the synod. At this time the poet was teaching at Gairney Bridge, as we have already seen, and having procured a substitute for his school, entered the Theological Hall of the Associate Synod at Kinross. The class was held in the large room of what is now the Lochleven Inn, and was conducted by Professor Swanston, concerning whom everyone agrees that he was not only an able professor, but " wise, scholarly and, above all, attractive as a Christian to the young."

The students then lived with the friends of their denomination in the district, and Bruce was welcomed into the family of Mr. Henderson of Turfhills, whose son George was also a student. David Greig, George Lawson, Alexander Bennet, Andrew Swanston and others, who in after years eminently filled the pulpits of the Burgher Synod, associated with Bruce at the " Hall." To know the young poet was to love him. He became not only a great favourite with all the students at the " Hall," but was entwined in the affections of the professor himself, who treated him rather as a brother or son than a mere church member or student. While residing at Turfhills, Bruce in spite of the delicate state of his health, must have been extremely comfortable and happy. His lines had fallen to him in pleasant places. George Henderson, his companion at College, who is celebrated in " Lochleven " under the name of " Laelius," was his daily companion,

THE OLD SECESSION CHURCH BUILDING—DIVINITY
HALL AND MANSE

Occupied by Rev. Professor Swanston, the poet's teacher,
minister and friend, in Kinross

and all that was beautiful and lovely in family life was brought to play upon the spirit of the poet.

> Nor shall the Muse forget thy friendly heart,
> O Laelius ! partner of my youthful hours ;
> How often, rising from the bed of peace,
> We would walk forth to meet the summer morn,
> Inhaling health and harmony of mind ;
> Philosophers and friends ; while science beam'd
> With ray divine as lovely on our minds
> As yonder orient sun, whose welcome light
> Reveal'd the vernal landscape to the view.
> Yet oft, unbending from more serious thought,
> Much of the looser follies of mankind,
> Hum'rous and gay, we'd talk, and much would laugh
> While, ever and anon, their foibles vain
> Imagination offer'd to our view.

Michael Bruce and George Henderson, along with other fellow-students, were wont to take frequent walks along the Kirkgate to the Old Churchyard by the loch side, rehearsing their Hall "sermons," and exchanging ideas on things in general. Long known in the county as freeholders, the Hendersons were of the old stock of Covenanters. Many a bold deed was executed by chiefs of that race in the past in supporting the good cause of freedom in religious thought and action. " At the time," says Dr. Grosart, " of the noble stand for the ' true Evangel,' made by the Erskines and their compeers, as was to be expected, James Henderson adhered to them ; and at the very first meeting at Gairney Bridge was chosen as an elder. All the preliminary meetings—and they were numerous—were held at Turfhills ; so much so, that one room in the house was known as the Presbytery's room. Many a heartfelt prayer, many wrestlings for the welfare of Scotland, many burning words to Christ for souls, and to souls for Christ, were spoken from one of the open windows—hundreds, even thousands, coming from far and near to hang upon the lips of such men as Ebenezer Erskine of Stirling, Ralph Erskine of Dunfermline, Thomas Mair of Orwell, James Fisher of Kinclaven, William Wilson of Perth, and Alexander Moncrieff of Abernethy—a noble band, to whom Scotland owes more than ever will be known until ' the great Day.' ' "

It was into this family—one of the old stamp of godliness, kingly men and mother-of-Lemuel-like women— that Michael Bruce was received. It must have had peculiar attractions to him. There were the traditions of the Covenanters ; there was an hereditary taste for ballad-lore and the " auld manners " of " auld lang syne "; there was generous hospitality ; there was a fellow-student like-minded ; and above all and about all an atmosphere of real godliness, of no austere but contrari-wise joyous sort. In all his connections with his friends to whom we have referred in our narrative Michael Bruce seems to have been singularly fortunate in his circum-stances, and in no way can the expression " neglected genius " be applied to him. That delicacy of constitution with which he was born showed itself very mournfully during the first session at the Hall, and he was advised by good Professor Swanston to refrain from study altogether for a time.

His friend Dryburgh wrote to him from Dysart on 1st April, 1766 :—" I was very sorry to learn from Mr. George Henderson, who spent a night with us last week, that you thought yourself worse since you were here. Nothing, be assured, would be more agreeable to me than to hear of your recovery. I heard, also, that Mr. Swanston has been advising you to give up your studies altogether. I really think it your duty to comply with this advice, at least, till you see how you are." Of all his college companions, Bruce was most attached to William Dryburgh who was a youth of extraordinary piety, and alas ! like the poet also a youth of consumptive tendency. With

49

the prospect of a short earthly career before them, and
" heirs together of the grace of life," they were drawn
towards each other by sympathies and regards such
as none but pious minds can feel.

Dryburgh, who felt such a kindly interest in the
welfare of the poet as to tender him such loving advice,
was soon withdrawn from this earthly scene into the
presence of his Lord and King, whom they both loved,
and from Whom they can now never be separated. Soon
after writing the above letter, Dryburgh died in his
eighteenth year, being followed by Bruce less than a year
after. Our poet keenly felt the death of his friend,
and upon receiving intelligence of the event at Forest
Mill, addressed a very affectionate letter to his friend
Pearson. " I have not many friends," says he, " but
I love them well. Death has been among the few I have.
Poor Dryburgh ! but he is happy. I expected to have
been his companion through life, and that we should have
stept into the grave together ; but heaven has seen meet
to dispose of him otherwise. What think you of this
world ? I think it is very little worth. You and I have
not a great deal to make us fond of it ; and yet I would
not change my condition with any unfeeling fool in the
universe, if I were to have his dull hard heart into the
bargain. Farewell, my rival in immortal hope ! my companion, I trust, for eternity ! Though far distant, I take
thee to my heart ; souls suffer no separation from the
obstruction of matter, or distance of place. Oceans may
roll between us, and climates interpose in vain—the
whole material creation is no bar to the winged mind.
Farewell ! through boundless ages fare thee well ! May'st
thou shine when the sun is darkened ! May'st thou live
and triumph when time expires ! It is at least possible
we may no more meet in this foreign land, this gloomy
apartment in the universe of God. But there is a better
world in which we may meet to part no more. Adieu."

Referring to this letter Dr. Mackelvie says : " Genuine grief, like genuine love, is poetical, for the one is the natural offspring of the other ; and prose is too cold and sluggish to be the vehicle of either passion when roused. In grief, as in love, the most dull and stupid are sometimes poetical without being aware of it. But Bruce was a poet by nature, and, therefore, a poet upon all occasions. Expecting his verse to live after he himself was dead and his prose forgotten, he resolved that if his memory should survive, Dryburgh's should survive along with it, and that the world should know how much he loved his friend, and how much his friend was worthy of his love."

Alas ! we fondly thought that Heaven designed
　His bright example mankind to improve.
All they should be was pictured in his mind—
　His thoughts were virtue, and his heart was love.

Calm as the summer sun's unruffled face,
　He looked unmoved on life's precarious game,
And smiled at mortals toiling in the chase
　Of empty phantoms—opulence and fame.

Steady he followed virtue's onward path,
　Inflexible to error's devious way ;
And firm at last in hope and fixèd faith,
　Through death's dark vale he trod without dismay.

Whence, then, these sighs ? and whence this falling tear,
　To sad remembrance of his merit just ?
Still must I mourn ! for he to me was dear,
　And still is dear, though buried in the dust.

Bruce continued his studies till the close of the Hall in 1766, and on his return to Gairney Bridge, finding that a report was circulated against his substitute, was so vexed and annoyed that he gave up his school, and accepted another at Forest Mill, about fifteen miles south-west of Kinross, and a few miles from Tillicoultry.

Chapter VII

BRUCE AT FOREST MILL

When Bruce left Kinross with all its happy associations the prospect before him was gloomy indeed. Dr. Grosart visited the spot where Bruce taught ; and " from inquiries made and faint memories revived," he remarks : " We can understand that to one so predisposed to consumption, and, spite of resistance, apt to be overcome with melancholy, it was a poor change for Gairney Bridge and Classlochie. The school was low-ceiled, earthen-floored, chilly, musty, close. Outside, dreary spaces of moor flushed with heather, skirted with sombre pines—the ' wild ' of his ' Elegy to Spring.' Society uncongenial ; children dense, stupid, backward. The only ray of sunlight was the wistful care of him by a daughter of the family with whom he lodged, whose name was Mill."

As Bruce was crossing the Devon on his way to Forest Mill, his horse stumbled, and he was immersed in the stream. He did not receive any injury beyond a thorough " wetting." When he arrived at his lodgings he had to be put to bed, and, with that pity which dwells in womankind, Miss Mill, one of the daughters of the family with whom he lodged, did all she could for his restoration and comfort. Soon he was able to begin the school, and Miss Mill saw that it was well warmed, even placing boards on the ground where his feet rested, to keep them from the clammy floor. But all was in vain. From that time he grew weaker and weaker, and none felt more than he did himself that his career on earth would soon be run. The country round about was one of the bleakest possible, and seeing all this, the poet seems to have fallen into a settled state of melancholy. Whatever hopes of health and success he may have entertained when he went to Forest Mill were doomed to disappointment. Life began to lose its charms, but he bore up manfully. This world did not circumscribe his aspirations ; and now when earthly glories were to be eclipsed in early dawn, he could say, as he had often said before—" The Supreme Wisdom has seen this meet, and the Supreme Wisdom cannot err." There is a pathetic tone and a vein of humour in many of his letters. It was from Forest Mill some interesting letters of the poet were written, and our biography would scarcely be complete unless we reproduced one or two here. To his friend, Mr. Arnot of Portmoak, he wrote, on July 28th, 1766 :—" Dear Sir,—It is an observation of some of your philosophers, that it is much better for man to be ignorant of than to know the future incidents of his life ; for, says one, if some men were beforehand acquainted with the terrible miseries that await them, they would be as miserable in fearing (and I believe more so) than in suffering. Again, when we are in expectation of any good, we paint all the agreeable to ourselves, and dwell in fancy on it ; nor can we be convinced, but by experience, that everything here is of a mixed nature. When this so long expected convenience arrives, we can scarcely believe it [is] what we hoped for, and, in truth, it is very different. Many a disappointment of this kind have I met with. What I enjoyed of anything was always in the hope of it. I expected to be happy here, but I am not ; and my sanguine hopes are the reason of my disappointment. The easiest part of my life is past, and I was never happy. I sometimes compare my condition with that of others, and imagine if I were in theirs I should be well. But is not everybody thus ? Perhaps he whom I envy thinks he would be glad to change with me, and yet neither would be better for the change. Since it is so, let us, my friend, moderate our hopes and fears, resign ourselves to the will of Him who ' doeth all things well,' and Who hath assured us that He careth for us ; and rejoice in hope of the glory that is to be revealed, and which will infinitely surpass our greatest expectations.

> . . . . . " Hoc res est una
> Solaque qui facere possit et servare beatum.

" Things are not very well in this world, but they are pretty well. They might have been worse ; and, as they are, may please us who have but a few short days to use them. This scene of affairs, tho' a very perplexed, is a very short one, and in a little all will be cleared up. Let us endeavour to please God, our fellow-creatures, and ourselves. In such a course of life we shall be as happy as we can be in such a world as this. Thus, you who cultivate your farm with your own hands, and I who teach a dozen blockheads for bread, may be happier than he who, having more than he can use, tortures his brain to invent new methods of killing himself with the superfluities. But whither do I ramble ? I forget that I am telling you what you know better than I do. But I must say something. I hope to hear from you an account of your journey to Edinr., etc.

" I have wrote a few lines of a descriptive poem, *cui titulus est* ' Lochleven.' You may remember (as Mr. M——r says) you hinted such a thing to me ; so I have set about it, and you may expect a dedication. I hope it will soon be *finished*, as I every week add two lines, blot out six, and alter eight. You shall hear the plan when I know it myself. My complts. to the family. Farewell. —I am yours, etc., MICHAEL BRUCE."

Writing to Mr. David Pearson again, he says :—

" The next letter you receive from me, *if ever you receive another*, will be dated 1767. . . . I lead a melancholy kind of life in this place. I am not fond of company. But it is not good that a man be still alone ; and here I have no company but what is worse than solitude. If I had not a lively imagination, I believe I should fall into a state of stupidity and delirium. I have some evening scholars, the attending of whom, though few, so fatigues me that the rest of the night I am quite dull and low-spirited. Yet I have some lucid intervals, in the time of which I can study pretty well."

There must have been lucid intervals, as he himself designates them, and a bright light must often have flashed across his path, like the light which shineth more and more unto the perfect day. Sad it was to relinquish the friendships of earth ; but would not these flourish in a happier clime, and were not friends gone before longing to receive him at the golden gates ? Fond admirers told him he would yet stand as high on the rolls of fame as ever did Addison or Pope ; but would he not soon be crowned with the laurels that never fade ? Such enlivening thoughts chased away despair, beguiled the tedium of day school and night school, and made him at times forget the disease that was slowly but surely doing its work. Intervals of relief he enjoyed in living over again the days of boyhood. Memory brooded o'er the scenes of his birth, and how fondly these were cherished, the concluding lines of his " Lochleven," composed at this time, and dedicated to Mr. Arnot, affectingly attest :—

Thus sung the youth, amid unfertile wilds
And nameless deserts, unpoetic ground,
Far from his friends he strayed, recording thus
The dear remembrance of his native fields
To cheer the tedious night, while slow disease
Preyed on his pining vitals, and the blasts
Of dark December shook his humble cot.

Certain features are omitted in this poem which strike the reader who is acquainted with the scene it depicts ; but we have no intention of entering into a formal criticism of it or any of Bruce's poetry at this stage of our narrative. We shall do so when considering his writings.

The activity of Bruce's mind was not affected by the slow disease from which he was suffering, but the effort of mind which his composition of " Lochleven " had called forth seems to have been too much for his shattered frame, and he was compelled almost immediately after it was finished to relinquish his school. His young heart yearned for home—"for a mother's hand, a mother's face, a mother's kiss, a mother's love." He walked all the way home, a distance of fully twenty miles, resting only for a little at Turfhills. Then he betook himself to the kindly influences of home and friendship. And here again he breathed the atmosphere of love which was characteristic of the family circle, so that it might be said in all reverence that God, from Whom he received his poetic genius, was ever near him. While the poet was a man to create friendship wherever he went, in time of trouble he looked to the only source for comfort and solace, to One Who was, and still is, the greatest friend and Saviour of mankind.

Chapter VIII

LIFE'S CLOSING SCENES

Bruce was kindly and tenderly cared for at home, but his life upon earth was drawing to a close. Kinnesswood, which is proverbial for mists, was by no means a desirable place for a consumptive patient to reside in, but what more natural than that he should be nursed by those to whom he was so dear ? The vapours which often shroud the hills proved too much for him. In " Lochleven " he thus refers to these vapours :

> The twilight trembles o'er the misty hills,
> Trinkling with dew.

He had no hope of recovering, but within there was a golden hope of yearning after immortality, as he himself serenely sings in his pathetic and tender " Elegy written in Spring "—the last poem he wrote in contemplation of his approaching death :—

> There let me sleep, forgotten in the clay,
>   When death shall shut these weary, aching eyes ;
> Rest in the hope of an eternal day,
>   Till the long night is gone, and the last morn arise.

Bruce sent his " Ode to Spring " when finished to his friend, Mr. George Henderson, with a view to apprize him of his expected departure to another and a better world. It is a matter of regret, we believe, that the

LIFE OF MICHAEL BRUCE

original MS. of this beautiful poem has gone a-missing from
the family papers of the Hendersons of Turfhills.

About the same time that Bruce apprized his friend
Mr. Henderson, in verse, of his approaching dissolution,
he addressed his friend Pearson to the same effect in
prose , taking a stanza out of the same ode as a motto :—

If morning dreams presage approaching fate,
   And morning dreams, as poets tell, are true,—
Led by pale ghosts, I enter death's dark gate,
   And bid this life and all the world adieu.

" A few mornings ago as I was taking a walk on an
eminence which commands a view of the Forth, with the
vessels sailing along, I sat down, and taking out my Latin
Bible, opened by accident at a place in the book of Job,
ix. 23, ' Now my days are passed away as swift ships.'
Shutting the book, I fell a-musing on this affecting comparison. Whether the following happened to me in a
dream or waking reverie, I cannot tell ; but I fancied myself on the bank of a river or sea ; the opposite side was
hid from view, being involved in clouds of mist. On the
shore stood a multitude which no man could number,
waiting for passage. I saw a great many ships take in
passengers, and several persons going about in the garb
of pilots, offering their service. Being ignorant and
curious to know what all these things meant, I applied to
a grave old man, who stood by, giving instructions to the
departing passengers. His name, I remember, was the
Genius of Human Life. ' My son,' said he, 'you stand on
the banks of the stream of Time. All these people are
bound for *Eternity*, that " undiscovered country from
whence no traveller ever returns." The country is very
large and is divided into two parts : the one is called the
Land of Glory, the other the Kingdom of Darkness.
The names of those in the garb of pilots are *Religion*,

58

Virtue, Pleasure. They who are so wise as to choose Religion for their guide have a safe though frequently a rough passage; they are at last landed in the happy climes where sighing and sorrow for ever flee away. They have likewise a secondary director, *Virtue*, but there is a spurious virtue who pretends to govern by himself; but the wretches who trust to him, as well as those who have Pleasure for their pilot, are either shipwrecked, or are cast away in the Kingdom of Darkness. *But the vessel in which you must embark approaches; you must begone.* Remember what depends upon your conduct.' No sooner had he left me, than I found myself surrounded by those pilots I mentioned before. Immediately I forgot all that the old man said to me, and seduced by the fair promises of *Pleasure*, chose him for my director. We weighed anchor with a fair gale; the sky serene, the sea calm. Innumerable little isles lifted their green heads around us, covered with trees in full blossom; dissolved in stupid mirth, we were carried on, regardless of the past, of the future unmindful. On a sudden the sky was darkened, the winds roared, the sea raged; red rose the sand from the bottom of the troubled deep. The angel of the waters lifted up his troubled voice. At that instant a strong ship passed by; I saw *Religion* at the helm. ' Come out from these!' he cried. I and a few others threw ourselves out into his ship. The wretches we left were now tossed on the swelling deep. The waters on every side poured through the riven vessel. They cursed the Lord; when, lo! a fiend rose from the deep, and in a voice like distant thunder, thus spoke: ' I am Abaddon, the first-born of death; ye are my prey. Open, thou abyss, to receive them.' As he thus spoke they sunk, and the waves closed over their heads. The storm was turned into a calm, and we heard a voice saying, ' Fear not, I am with you. When you pass through the waters they shall not overflow you.' Our hearts were filled with joy. I was engaged in discourse with one of my new companions, when one from the top of the mast cried out, ' Courage, my friends, I see the fair haven, the land that is yet afar off.' Looking up, I found that it was a certain friend who had mounted up for the benefit of contemplating the country before him. Upon seeing *you*, I was so affected that I started and awakened. Farewell, my friend, farewell."

The above allegory reminds us not a little of Addison's " Vision of Mirza." Latterly the most Bruce could do was to walk out and sit down on the tuft of grass in the garden already referred to. The tender assiduities of parents were lavished, but all in vain. The last earthly hope withered, and he prepared to die. His last days were spent in meditation, and in conversing and corresponding with friends. To concentrate his mind on the dread realities of eternity he revised his poem on " The Last Day "—one of his college productions. Before his strength failed altogether he transferred most of that poem enlarged and improved to his volume of MSS., the loss of which is greatly to be deplored, as it contained a number of his poems, including his " Ode to the Cuckoo," " Hymns " and " Paraphrases," and " Elegy in Spring." His cheerfulness and even his playful humour remained to the last—nay, he could even indulge his jocularity in contemplation of his speedy dissolution ! With him the bitterness of death had long been over. He had learned from Christian parents, as well as from the oracles of God, that to those who reposed themselves in Christ, death was a glorious, a happy exchange ; the present sufferings were not to be compared with the glory that should be revealed in him. His little pocket Bible was his constant companion, and very sweetly and modestly would he talk about certain portions of it to those who visited him. One morning in June, on hearing from his mother of the sudden death of his beloved minister and professor,

Swanston, his cheerfulness was overcast for a moment.
With ruthless hand the fell destroyer had broken many
tender ties. But this is Bruce's song :—

A few short years of evil past,
    We reach the happy shore,
Where death-divided friends at last
    Shall meet to part no more.

He himself tells us how he used to sit in the Old Churchyard of Portmoak reading Young's " Night Thoughts "
and Gray's " Elegy " ; and we can picture to ourselves
the pensive youth directing his solitary path along Lochleven's shore to meditate upon the most momentous of
all subjects. The flickering moonbeams lighting up the
gloomy towers and distant shores of the lake, and opening
vistas in the clouds that extend away into the blackness
of darkness, the wind sighing and moaning across the
troubled waters, the waves in melancholy dash breaking
upon the shore, the plaintive scream of birds which seem
to find no rest—all these circumstances combined to form
a scene suggestive of what is perhaps the most pathetic
verse of his touching elegy :—

I hear the helpless wail, the shriek of woe,—etc.

In his last illness, one of his fellow students, the late Dr.
Lawson, of Selkirk, who happened to be preaching as a
candidate for the congregation of Mr. Mair at Milnathort,
called upon him. Mr. Lawson found the poet in bed,
" very pale, his eyes large and lustrous, but delighted to
see his unexpected visitor." Mr. Lawson observed to him
that he was glad to find him so cheerful. " And why," said
he, with noble trustfulness, " should not a man be cheerful
on the verge of heaven ? " " But," said his friend, " you
look so emaciated, I am afraid you cannot last long."
Quickly, and with a flash of the humour of his healthful

days, he answered, " You remind me of the story of the
Irishman who was told that his hovel was about to fall ;
and I answer with him, ' Let it fall, it is not mine ' ; or
perhaps his words were, ' it is not *me*.' " Soon after this,
on the 5th of July, 1767, in the flower of his youth, Bruce
" imperceptibly fell asleep " in death, aged twenty-one
years and three months. His Bible was found upon his
pillow, marked down at Jer. xxii. 10, " Weep ye not for
the dead, neither bemoan him," and on the blank leaf
was written—

> 'Tis folly to rejoice and boast
> How small a price my Bible cost.
> The day of judgment will make clear
> 'Twas very cheap—or very dear.

LAST RESTING PLACE OF THE POET

The remains of our poet were laid in the churchyard
of Portmoak, in the very centre of the scene which has
been consecrated by his muse to the memory of Mr. Wm.
Arnot.

> Hail and farewell, blest youth ! soon hast thou left
> This evil world. Fair was thy thread of life ;
> But quickly by the envious Sisters shorn.
> Thus have I seen a rose with rising morn
> Unfold its glowing bloom, sweet to the smell
> And lovely to the eye ; when a keen wind
> Hath torn its blushing leaves and laid it low,
> Stripp'd of its sweets—Ah ! so,
> So Daphnis fell ! long ere his prime he fell !
> Nor left he on these plains his peer behind.

Portmoak burying-ground surrounds the Parish Kirk,
gradually sloping toward the loch, and the most prominent

TO THE
MEMORY OF
MICHAEL BRUCE.
WHO WAS BORN AT KINNESWOOD IN 1746
AND DIED WHILE A STUDENT
IN CONNECTION WITH THE SECESSION CHURCH
IN THE 21ST YEAR OF HIS AGE

THE POET'S MONUMENT IN PORTMOAK KIRKYARD
Erected by Rev. Dr. Mackelvie of Balgedie

object in it is the chaste monument which rises over the grave of Michael Bruce, the bard of Lochleven. The monument is in the form of a neat sarcophagus, and was erected to the memory of the poet in 1842, by Dr. Mackelvie, out of the profits of his edition of Bruce's poems. It took the place of a not very graceful obelisk about eight feet in height, which was erected in 1812, chiefly through the kind efforts of Dr. Baird, Principal of the University of Edinburgh. The present monument bears the following long inscription :—

TO THE

MEMORY OF

MICHAEL BRUCE

WHO WAS BORN AT KINNESSWOOD IN 1746,

AND DIED WHILE A STUDENT

IN CONNECTION WITH THE SECESSION CHURCH,

In the 21st Year of his Age.

Meek and gentle in spirit, sincere and unpretending in his Christian deportment, refined in intellect, and elevated in character, he was greatly beloved by his friends, and won the esteem of all ; while his genius, whose fire neither poverty nor sickness could quench, produced those odes, unrivalled for simplicity and pathos, which have shed an undying lustre on his name.

Early, bright, transient, chaste as morning dew,
He sparkled, and exhaled, and went to heaven.

Near Bruce's grave is that of his affectionate biographer —Dr. Mackelvie—so near that, as has been well said, with the change of names, the lines of Sir Walter Scott on Fox and Pitt may be applied :—

Drop on Bruce's grave the tear—
'Twill trickle to Mackelvie's bier.

The Portmoak churchyard possesses many interesting features, but we must not linger over them.

APPEARANCE AND CHARACTER OF THE POET

We get a glimpse of Bruce when he was a young man from Dr. Mackelvie. " His appearance," he says, " indicated his tendency to phthisis. He was slenderly made, with a long neck and narrow chest ; his skin white and shining ; his cheeks tinged with red, rather than ruddy ; his hair yellowish, and inclined to curl. Such is the description of him which we have received from some of those who were his schoolfellows, and upon whom his interesting appearance, and aptitude to learn, seem to have made an indelible impression." His character has been well brought out in the inscription which appears on his monument. While he was depressed in spirits during the first stages of his illness, his wonted sprightliness returned, and Dr. Mackelvie tells us " he conversed with his visitors as if he had been still in the heyday of health, and in the enjoyment of the brightest prospects which this life can afford. Had he been spared, he must have enjoyed existence, for he was largely furnished by nature with the elements of happiness ; but we are persuaded that, to afford him suitable gratification, he would have required more money than was likely to fall to his share. His fine perception of the beautiful, both in nature and art, would have naturally led him to provide himself with things which minds less refined would have considered trifles ; and to embellish what he possessed in a manner which, by ordinary men, would have been deemed extravagant. Throughout Bruce's poetry every discerning reader perceives tenderness of sentiment, beauty of thought, and felicity of diction : and, judging from these qualities in his compositions, he is likely to expect that the poet himself would be characterized by elegance of manner. But this was not the case. Not

65

F

that Michael Bruce was either rude or coarse, but he was modest to excess, and he never improved his provincial pronunciation, a circumstance which conveyed to those not intimately acquainted with him an impression of rusticity. He had, besides, an unbounded love of truth ; and consequently would indulge in no praise or blame which was not fully called for. He loathed affectation, and would not put forth even just claims to merit, lest he should be suspected of advancing unwarrantable pretensions. To this feeling the retention of his provincial dialect is, in all probability, to be ascribed, being afraid that his early companions, whom he continued to cherish with all the ardour of first love, might ascribe his correctness of speech to a desire of being thought the *fine gentleman*."

A striking feature in our poet's character was the intensity of feeling with which he loved all his friends, who loved him as sincerely in return. But of all his characteristics, his piety was the most distinguishing. This trait in his character has been fully touched upon by us already. " Whether any virtues would have accompanied me," Bruce wrote on one occasion, " in a more elevated station is uncertain, but that a number of vices, of which my sphere is incapable, would have been its attendants, is unquestionable." This is a humble confession. Bruce would have been the last himself to lay claim to any virtues or gifts he possessed. He knew the source whence they sprang. Early in life he opened his heart to Christ, and under that transforming divine influence, the life and character which we now behold were developed, just as the lily, at the impulse of the living germ within it, bursts out into beauty and life.

> To things immortal time can do no wrong ;
> And that which never is to die, forever must be young.

Piety is almost synonymous with charity or love, and the finest picture that has been presented to us, or ever will be presented to us, of this grace, will be found in the Bible, from which so many men of genius have borrowed their light. Genius is not within the reach of all, but this true piety is. It was a power in Bruce's life, and what a value he placed upon it is seen in the following verse from his pen :—

> For she has treasures greater far
> Than east or west unfold,
> And her reward is more secure
> Than is the gain of gold.

Bruce's character was transparent throughout ; there was nothing to dim its lustre, and his life has been described by the late Dr. Robert Chambers as one of the most beautiful chapters in our literary history.

To this we may add that of Michael Bruce, more than any other, it may be said that his poetry was his life ; his whole heart and soul were in his verses, and no one reading his writings carefully can fail to appreciate his character. Although his life presents little of incident or adventure, what we find in his writings and correspondence might be regarded as a kind of autobiography. Short as his life was, it was complete, and fulfilled its God-given mission. As the Rev. Mr. Stephen remarks, " We mark how lovingly, how unweariedly, and with what abiding success that mission is fulfilled."

Chapter IX

END OF THE AGED PARENTS

The autumn of the same year in which Michael Bruce
died, Logan visited Kinnesswood, and prevailed upon
the friends of the poet to furnish him with his manuscripts, which he knew were in a state of preparation for
the press ; as also the letters written to and by him, and
particularly those which he himself had addressed to him.
In compliance with this request, every person who had
ever been known to correspond with Bruce was impor-
tuned to furnish Logan with his letters, which was in every
case done. None of these were ever seen again, although
Logan gave the assurance that they would be carefully
returned. At the same time Logan obtained the MS.
volume from Bruce's father for the purpose of publishing
Bruce's poems, so that the old parents might derive some
pecuniary benefit from the publication. After frequent
applications from the friends of Bruce, and an interval
of three years had elapsed, Logan, without any mention
of himself as Editor, published a volume, entitled " Poems
on Several Occasions by Michael Bruce.'' Its stinted
appearance confounded the friends of the departed poet,
many of whom had possessed opportunities of knowing
the bent of his genius, and also the subjects of his effusions.
The volume edited by Logan, to the surprise of all who
knew the eminently pious character of Bruce, and the
Christian tendency of his most valued compositions,
contained scarcely a line, except in one out of nineteen

68

poems, indicating a mind really impressed with " things unseen." It is recorded of his pious father, when he had glanced over the meagre contents of the volume, that he burst into tears, and, in reference to the many spiritual compositions with which his lamented son had cheered his last moments of comparative strength, exclaimed, " Where are my son's Gospel Sonnets ? " It was at once felt that, while Logan had happily published enough for placing Bruce in the classical ranks of the poets of England, he had dealt cruelly and unfaithfully with the sacred deposit entrusted to him as a professed friend of the lamented poet. An effort was made to regain possession of the manuscript volume, but without success. Scraping with difficulty a few shillings together, the aged and impoverished father of the poet visited Edinburgh, for the first time in his life, and finding Logan, obtained from him a few loose papers, containing the first draft of " Lochleven," " The Last Day " etc. ; but insisting on the restoration of his son's manuscript volume, containing his collection of transcribed pieces, he found Logan unable or unwilling to furnish it, and had to return broken-hearted to his humble cottage, with nothing from Logan to cheer him but the cold expression of " *his fear that the servants had singed fowls* " with the missing volume. The father of Bruce never recovered from this. He died two years after his sad journey to Edinburgh, on the 19th July, 1772. This saintly man on his death-bed was never heard to say anything worse of Logan than that he regretted his dishonourable conduct, but he freely forgave him, and hoped God would forgive him too. An account of the venerable elder from the pen of his old apprentice, David Pearson, appeared in one of the periodicals of that day. Michael's mother lived to the year 1798 ; and it is to the everlasting honour of Principal Baird that he contributed largely to her support, and in the end paid her funeral expenses. " Seldom has a human heart been more grateful to God," remarks Dr. Mackelvie, " and the agents He employs in the diffusion of His bounties, than that of this old woman for these unexpected supplies. She was seen by an acquaintance, shortly after receiving them, going about the village with a basket on her arm, containing a number of small loaves. When asked what she was about she replied, ' When heaven is raining so plentifully upon me, I may ay let twa or three draps fa' on my puir neighbours.' "

Mr. Hervey, merchant, Stirling, had a great respect for Bruce's parents, and was very kind to Mrs. Bruce. At the time when Dr. Baird acknowledged the truth as to the real authorship of the " Ode to the Cuckoo," Mr. Hervey wrote to Mr. John Eirrel : " He (Dr. Baird) has found ' The Cuckoo ' to be Bruce's and has the original in his own handwriting." The circumstances of John Hervey's acquaintance with the Poems of Bruce, and the impression made upon him by reading, for the first time, the Elegy in Spring, are finely related by Dr. Mackelvie. The devout and cultured Stirling merchant—looking forward to an early summons into the Great Presence—found in the Elegy a power to sustain and cheer him which he had never before experienced from any source—outside the inspired Word itself. This incident led Mr. Hervey, along with a few Stirling friends, to form the project of bringing out a new edition of the Poems with what was still a desideratum, a Memoir of their Author. The purpose was only relinquished when it was understood that the task had been undertaken by Dr. Baird. We need hardly add that any service in his power, in collecting materials for the Principal's edition, was most cordially rendered. Here we might refer to a pathetic incident in connection with a window which Mrs. Bruce expressly wished inserted in her cottage. To this window a peculiar interest was attached by a simple and touching reference to it in a letter from Mr. Birrel to Mr.

Hervey. " Ann " (the poet's mother), he writes, " insists upon having a window cut out in the south wall, in order that she may see Lochleven and Stirling, for she says that though she never saw either Mr. Hervey or Mr. Telford " (to whom she felt indebted for many acts of genuine kindness) " yet she likes to see the airt they come frae, and this window must be cut out, though it should be at her own expense."

On one occasion when a cuckoo was shot, and Mrs. Bruce was looking at it with some of the villagers, she asked—" Will that be the bird our Michael made a song about ? " But what an amount of controversy has been raised about this and other poems of Bruce in consequence of Logan's conduct ! A small pamphlet upon the subject written by Mr. David Laing, and published in 1873, has been kindly sent to us by a friend, and in a letter which appears in it the writer, referring to the " Ode to the Cuckoo," says : " The authorship of the Ode seems to create as much interest among Scots as Homer's birthplace did among the Greeks." The " Ode to the Cuckoo " was familiar to the villagers of Kinnesswood long before it appeared in print. Bruce was in the habit, as was Burns, of writing copies of his poems and sending them to his friends, among whom David Pearson, an intimate friend of the poet, wrote to Dr. Anderson : " When I came to visit his father a few days after Michael's death, he went and brought forth his poem-book, and read the ' Ode to the Cuckoo ' and the ' Musiad,' at which the old man was greatly overcome." The result of investigation by many eminent literary men, including Principal George Husband Baird of Edinburgh University, Principal Shairp, Professor Davidson, John Bright, Dr. Grosart, and others, as well as more recently Dr. Julian in his " Dictionary of Hymnology," was all in favour of the claims made on behalf of Michael Bruce, and the reader will be justified in assuming that all the writings in this volume in prose or verse represent what are actually attributed to Bruce.

The following is a copy of the only letter known to exist written by Alexander Bruce, the poet's father. It is addressed to David Pearson in Pathhead. This letter is now exhibited in the Cottage Museum at Kinnesswood :—

KINNESSWOOD, *4th March*, 1765.

DEAR FRIEND,—I received your letter some time ago ; it was very welcome to me. I desire to sympathise with you and to recommend you to the care of the Great Physician who only can heal all our diseases and pains. I would have you consider that affliction springeth not out of the dust ; all is ordered by Infinite Wisdom, and all is designed for the real good and advantage of the people of God. There is a time coming, and that ere long, when the righteous shall be removed out of all their troubles, and all sorrow and sighing shall fly away. Strive to submit to the will of God, who knows what is best for you ; and though no chastising for the present seemeth joyous, yet it henceforth yieldeth the peaceable fruits of righteousness to them who are exercised thereby, and " our light afflictions which are but for a moment work out for us a far more exceeding and eternal weight of glory." He chastens us for our profit, and therefore we ought not to despise the chastening of the Lord, nor to be weary of His correction. Whom He loves He chastens, and if we be without this, then are we bastards and not sons. At present we see but the dark side of the cloud ; yet, to the upright, light will arise ; though he be in darkness, yet joy cometh in the morning. Strive to have your heart weaned from the world, and count all but loss for the excellency of the knowledge of Jesus Christ our Lord. It is good news to the people of God that our Lord Jesus has overcome death, so that it is a vanquished enemy, and they need not fear to go down to the grave, for He will be with them, to sustain them for ever. May the God of all comfort strengthen and support you by His Spirit in Christ Jesus

Is the wish and prayer of your constant friend,

ALEXANDER BRUCE.

END OF THE AGED PARENTS

A DIALOGUE ON SCHOOL FEES

The following dialogue on his school experiences gives some idea of the poet's circumstances at Gairney Bridge, and his invincible sprightliness of spirit :—

As I was about to enter on my labours for the week, an old fellow like a Quaker came up and addressed me thus :

Q. Peace be with you, friend.

M. Be you also safe.

Q. I have brought my son, Tobias, to thee, that thou mayest instruct him in the way that he should go.

M. He is welcome.

Q. Our brother Jacob telleth me that thou shewest thyself a faithful workman, hearing thy scholars oftener in a day than others, because thou hast few.

M. I presume I do.

Q. Verily, therein thou doest well : thou shalt not lose thy reward : it shall be given thee with the faithful in their day.

M. Ay, but, friend, I need somewhat in present possession.

Q. I understand you : thou wouldst have the prayers of the faithful.

M. Ay, and something more substantial ; in short, I must have two shillings per quarter for teaching your son, Tobias.

Q. Ah ! friend, I perceive thou lovest the mammon of unrighteousness : let me convince you of your sin.

M. Certainly, since thou seemest to be a most righteous man, who deemeth the servant worthy of his hire.

Q. Hearken unto my voice : Ezekiel, who was also called Holdfast, took but sixpence in the quarter, as thou callest it. He was a good man, but he sleepeth ; the faithful mourned for him. He catechised the children seven times a day. He was one of the righteous, yea, he was upright in his day save in the matter of ——

M. I still think that the labour you expect me to bestow on your son, Tobias, is worth two shillings a quarter.

Q. Two shillings ! Verily, friend, thou art an extortioner : yea, thou grindest the face of the poor : thou lovest filthy lucre. Thou hast respect unto this present world. *Coetera desunt.*

Chapter X

LETTERS BY MICHAEL BRUCE

IT is to be regretted that out of the vast number of letters written by Michael Bruce to his father and mother, Mr. Arnot of Portmoak, Mr. John Dun, David Pearson, James Campbell and others, between the years 1762 and 1767, so few remain to this day. Had these been obtainable they would have exhibited the strongest possible evidence in support of all that was necessary to settle the question so long debated. It is quite evident that circumstances were much against the retaining of old letters in the ordinary arrangements of small houses in the country. While those that John Logan secured during his unexpected visit to the village of Kinnesswood almost completed the total destruction of Bruce's letters, still we have a few left us which clearly show the kind of person Michael Bruce was, for in them we read the young poet's inner feelings, his mild humour and heaven-inspired truthfulness towards all who knew him. Besides, they express his faith in God and humble resignation to His will.

The following are copies of letters written by Michael Bruce from Edinburgh. The first is dated 12th April 1765, and is addressed to " Mr. David Arnot of Portmoak " :—

DEAR SIR,—You may remember you were inquiring the last time I had the pleasure of your company, what the Hutchinsonians are? Perhaps you know. I then did not, but have since learned something of them. Mr. Hutchinson, from whom they take their name, was an English gentleman, skilled in the Hebrew, and denied that the vowels or points belonged to the language. His reason for this was thought to be a disposition to criticise the sacred writings, in which he has been followed by some in our own nation. When once they have discarded the vowel points they may give very different readings, and consequently significations to many words. But what he was most famous for, was that he published a work in two volumes called, I think, *Principia Mosae*, a kind of commentary on the Old Testament, but particularly the Pentateuch and Psalms. The most part of the Old Testament, but specially those aforesaid, he holds (to be) symbolical, and in every sentence finds meanings which none but himself and some of his followers can see. Every part of the Psalms, he says, refers to the Messiah, or to use the words of an honest enthusiast of him, " He finds the Saviour in every word." The whole work is a confused piece of absurdity (they say who have read it) filled with trifling allegories and far-fetched conceits. To give one instance : The flaming sword placed at the gate of Paradise (according to him) was appointed to show the way to the tree of life, not to guard the way. It is said there are few passages of Scripture in which either in the translation he has not found some concealed meaning, or altered the translation for the sake of an allegory. You will let me know if this agrees with any hints you have met with of these people.

There is a manuscript of Longinus lately found in the library of the Benedictine Monks at Rome containing a comparison of some passages of Holy Writ with some (of) the heathen poets. I lately saw some extracts from it. Homer (says this judicious critic) makes the forest tremble at the approach of the Deity, but the Jewish poet says, " The earth did melt like wax at Thy presence," and indeed in every respect our Jehovah is superior to their Jupiter. And so he goes on in a great number of passages, always giving the preference to the Book of God.

I saw Mrs. Wallace this day, and received a letter to you. She has not yet got the escritoire or glass, but is to use diligence

I design to make one last effort on R. Hill before I give up my commission to resume it no more. I have not got Shep. Par. ; it was sold before I came over, not over a shilling. I ask your pardon for not sending your seeds before now. They were bought two weeks ago, but neglected to be sent by a forgetfulness in your affectionate

MICHAEL BRUCE.

EDINBURGH, 10*th April*, 1765.

P.S.—I remember one, who shall be nameless here, in a letter to a young man, has these words, " Si mihi, nil novi publici, etc., rescribis : nil boni vel jucundi, etc., communicas : vel tui fastidii vel ignaviae. Si non aegritudinis argumentum habebo : et tui a me nil amplius audiendi voluntas." Pray could such an one fail in the same article ? You may believe I am not a little chagrined on being so cruelly disappointed. I have sent the seeds and Mrs. W.'s letter.—11 o'clock night.

Letter addressed to Mr. Arnot of Portmoak. It is as follows :—

MY DEAR SIR,—I have sent the letter which you have undertaken to carry, spite of disappointments. It is open, but I believe the pleasure of reading it will not pay the trouble of carrying it. I do not choose to send a blank cover : therefore this (as I shall endeavour to fill it up somehow) shall never be called in question as to its letter-ality; that is to say, a return shall be due in law, and that (such as) it shall pass for an identical letter.

I have been reading Shaftesbury's " Characteristics," and shall transcribe for you what I think the best note I have found in it ; and it's this :

" It seems to me remarkable in our learned and elegant apostle, that he accommodates himself, according to his known character, to the humour and natural turn of the Ephesians, by writing to his converts in a kind of architect-style, and almost with a perpetual allusion to building, and to that majesty, order, and beauty of which this temple was a masterpiece ; as Eph. ii. 20-22 ; and so iii. 17, 18, etc., and iv. 16, etc." This is not a bad remark from one whom, notwithstanding my deference for the moderns, I look upon as little better than a deist.

I was about to entertain you with a character, not altogether unknown to you, of a talker or story-teller ; but I do not choose, merely for a little diversion, to deserve the reprehension of any person living.

I would have seen you this day (only I was troubled with a pain in the head), and perhaps I may see you as soon as this. I am yours affectionately,

MICHAEL BRUCE.

GAIRNEY BRIDGE, *May* 25th, 1765.

P.S.—You may put a date to the letter when you close it.

Note.—The *P.S.* refers to the enclosed letter Bruce is sending to Mr. Arnot from" Mr. Henderson," whose given name was George (from Turfhills).

The letter which Bruce wrote and sent with the poem " Daphnis " is to some extent explanatory. Yet it may be stated Portmoak farmhouse or " your town " stands close by the old kirkyard of Portmoak. The kirk was removed to its present position by the roadside, and a new burying-ground formed there. It was here that Bruce was buried. But " the auld kirkyard " remains where the kirk once stood, and also the Priory of Portmoak. It was on leaving this farmhouse and having to pass round the old burying-place where his companion and he had played amongst the gravestones, and now, alas ! was buried, that these thoughts filled his mind on his homeward walk across the moss to Kinnesswood.

There is a single leaf of another letter from Forest Mill of which Dr. Grosart remarks :—

The reference in the opening sentences is probably to the famous or infamous treatise of De Mandeville, " The Fable of the Bee, or Private Vices Public Benefits."

This following letter forms the concluding one of the Portmoak collection.

. . . I think it a most dry, unentertaining oddity, wanting that which makes a number of bad books too agreeable, I mean beauty of language. Many have erred in their pictures of human nature on the favourable side, but he on the opposite. I look on it as an attempt to prove that even God Himself, who rules in the kingdoms of the earth, cannot promote the wealth and strength of a nation but by means of luxury and profusion in all their most detestable branches. In his representations of men he differs very little from the *Candide* of Voltaire and the too witty Dr. Swift's *Hughnims*. But surely the contempt of the world is not a greater virtue than the contempt of our fellow-creatures is a vice. Dr. Young has said it, and it is truth. Make my compliments to your family, and believe me yours, etc.,

MICHAEL BRUCE.

FOREST MILL, 10*th December*, 1766.

P.S.—I design to be at Kinross Sabbath next, from whence I will send this. I will probably fetch Rollin to Gair[ney] Br[idge] and engage J. Campbell to carry him to you. By him you will write to me.

Bruce having a persuasion that his end was approaching, turned his thoughts to his friends Henderson and Pearson, the former in verse and the latter in prose. The following is a copy which has been preserved of his letter to David Pearson :—

FOREST MILL, 24*th Dec.* 1766.

DEAR FRIEND,—I received yours of the 17th current, and it is more than probable the next you receive from me (if ever you receive another) will bear date 1767. I can remember, Davie, I could write (or at least scratch) my name with the year 1752 below it. In that year I learned the elements of pencraft, and now, let me see, 'tis 1767-1752 = fourteen years since. A good term for one to be a scholar all that time. And what have I learnt? . Much that I need to unlearn. And I have need that one teach me this, that I know nothing.

I met the other day a drunken fool who grovelling lay upon the common road and raved at " Lady Fortune " in good terms—in good set terms, and yet a very fool. I helped him up. " I thank you, sir," quoth he, and then he drew a dial from his pouch, and gazing on it with unsteadfast eye, said very wisely, " It is ten o'clock. Thus may we see," quoth he, " how the world wags. 'Tis but an hour ago since it was nine, and in another hour 'twill be eleven, and so from hour to hour we ripe and ripe, and then from hour to hour we rot and rot, and thereby hangs a tale."

I tell you, Davie, I lead a melancholy kind of life in this place. I am not fond of company, but what is worse than solitude? If I had not a lively imagination, I believe I should fall into a state of stupidity and delirium. I have some evening scholars. The attending on them, tho' few, so fatigues me that the rest of the night I am quite dull and low-spirited. Yet I have some lucid intervals in the time of which I study pretty well.—I am yours as ever,

MICHAEL BRUCE.

P.S.—Let me hear from you with all convenient haste and at some length.

The following is an extract from a letter he sent from Forest Mill to David Pearson at Easter Balgedie, dated December, 1766 :—

On the day before St. Luke's fair in Kinross I made a voyage to the Inch[1] of Loch Leven, that being the time at which, you know, they bring the cattle out of it. The middle and highest part of it is covered with ruins. The foundations are visible enough, and it seems to have been a very large

[1] Bruce refers to a visit he made to St. Serf's Island in Lochleven.

building. The whole is divided into a great many little squares, from which it appears not an unplausible conjecture that not only a church, as they tell us, but a monastery had stood on it. To the westward of this, and in the lower ground, a deep dyke in the form of a trench is cut in the north and east side of a plain piece of ground not unlike a bowling green. I can give no guess for the use of this, though it evidently appears to be a work of art. I sought among the ruins and the stones of the little house which stands on it for some marks of inscriptions, but to no purpose. I could find nothing further to assist my conjectures. I would have examined [word wanting in MS.] had not the fishers been in such a hurry to be gone.

They who consider it in no other view than as capable of feeding a dozen or fourteen cattle, when their work was over would not stay a minute longer had it been to discover the great toe of St. Moak who is buried there. My description of it in the poem " Loch Leven," which by the way is now finished, runs thus :

> Fronting where Gairney pours its silent stream
> Into the lake, an island lifts its head,
> Grassy and wild,—etc.

TWO LETTERS BY DAVID ARNOT, THE LAIRD OF PORTMOAK

Letters by Mr. D. Arnot, the Laird of Portmoak, to M. Bruce—
Mr. Dryburgh

MY DEAR SIR,—I lately received your letter, in which you inquire respecting the health of our family. I have to say, in reply, that it is now as well as could be wished : but, alas, how frail is it ! and in this dubious path of life how liable every fleeting moment to fail us ! I am now desirous, in my turn, to hear that you are well, and successfully advancing in your studies. I hope and trust that you are still persisting in the course and pursuing the track which leads to the summit of learning, and consequently to honours. For there is no difficulty which labour may not obviate. Avail yourself of the opportunity which is now in your power. If neglected, it will never return. For as in the river wave presses upon wave, so in reference to Time does day upon day.[1] And as nothing is more shameful than the squandering away of time, so many, seriously, though too late, deplore it as a loss beyond all calculation. If in this spring-time of life you sow the seeds of learning, you have ground to expect hereafter a most abundant harvest,—a harvest agreeable to your parents, and honourable to yourself. Thus is it, my dear sir, that " he who would make the gain must take the pain."[2] Give to your studies whatever you take from sleep or recreation. This path has been trod by all who have ever rendered themselves illustrious for their distinguished learning. Degenerate souls steal their own time and that of others. They are a dishonour to their family and their country. Avoid them as you love yourself, and keep them at a distance. But, above all, let piety have the ascendant in your heart and pursuits ; and modesty, without which I value as nothing whatever may be mastered by laborious application. These are the groundwork of all true learning, by which whatever is reared on them upholds and proclaims its own stability. Without piety, what are learned men but bladders inflated with wind ? whereas the humble, endued with virtue, are agreeable to themselves and useful to others.

It was out of my power last week to answer your letter with regard to the book, and equally impossible is it for us to recall your letter. But what an abundance of books is there in the world ! In these, however, a systematic method should be observed, whether in consulting, reading, or purchasing,—not such books as are good, but such as are the best.

Enclosed you will receive a memorandum. When you

[1] " Truditur dies die "—Horace (Car, ii. 18). " Urget diem nox et dies noctem."—G.

[2] " Qui e nuce nucleum esse vult frangat nucem."—Plautus.

have perused the letters to R. Hill and J. Thomson, you will perceive their object and connection. These letters deliver to them sealed. Farewell, and regard me with affection.

DAVID ARNOT.

PORTMOAK, 24*th January*, 1763.

SIR,—I owe an answer to your most elegant lines, which you must account to be delayed hitherto, and not neglected. Neither are you to impute it to my want of love to you, nor regard for you, but to the fulness of my confidence in you, and the frequent occasions of seeing you, which now seem to be at an end in so far. On which account I am made to inquire where you now dwell, and what you are now conversant about, and whether or not this storm has freezed your pen, your hands, and feet, that we neither see you nor hear from you. As I said, I own my obligation to you for the regard you show for me and the deceast in your elegant composition, procured without any merit or good offices from me ; and I no less admire your singular vein and happy turn, whereby you're pleased and able not only to play the poet, but strenuously to imitate and equal those writers of this kind, in style, numbers, phrase, etc., whose fame will never decay. Learned sir, I desire and hope you will proceed with your essays, and that exercise and use may perfect him whom nature will have to be a poet.

" Sublimi feriam sidera vertice."[1]

Nothing hinders great attempts so much as delay. You now profess the study of divinity, and is not this divinity ? None can compose a learned, a grave and instructing poem save he that is above humanity. But I stop, knowing that they who are most deserving are the least fond of praise ; and I know nothing new which I can now impart to you, either for instruction or amusement.

Being abroad lately, I heard (you'll have feared it ere now) of Mr. D[ryburg]h,—his being infected seemingly with

[1] Horace.

his brother's mortal disease. A pain in his leg and a loss of appetite have seized him ; he goes not out. What may hinder you from making a step down to see him ? Alas ! had we our senses about us, we would see all our earthly relations and comforts fast decaying. But, alas ! man wishes life, that

" . . . 'scandam marmora
Locat sub ipsum fuuus et sepulcri immemor struit domos."

I know you'll be fearing the loss of him ; for it often happens that, as a whirlpool swallows up the rich ship in a surprise, so doth death such as have the better genius and learning above their years, beyond our expectation and before our desire.[1] But [illegible . . .] pray impart to me something that may be instructive in the now common calling of education or otherwise, as you have now the prize put into your hand of getting experience, etc.; and wherein I can serve you, command me. I am sensible that the charge of the education of children, as it is honourable, so it is heavy. Philip, king of Macedonia, had this view of it, and understood how much it serves the interest of virtue, when, in the letters he sent with his son to Aristotle, he testified how much he was indebted to the gods, not so much for a son being born to him, as for his being born at such a time, when he might be privileged with such a teacher.

As man is the most noble creature, so much the more pains are to be employed in cultivating of him. Surely the geniuses of youth will lie dormant as to all glorious and praiseworthy actions, if they be wanting which should rub them up, as the most fruitful soils will be barren without cultivation. But here there is surely much need of prudence, for as some ground requires the stronger plough, so another plot will be manured with an easy hand : and some think that there are none of such an evil, hard, and obstinate disposition, but they may be made tractable by serious and sedulous bringing up, if so be they understand themselves

[1] This fellow-student of Bruce died immediately after this date. See Elegy thereupon.

to be loved by them who educate and instruct them. The dispositions of some, when more roughly handled, or too much kept in, turn desperate, even as the exhalations, when pent up within the clouds, turn into thunder. With some, force must be used ; forbearance will do with the most. As in disease, they are the surest and safest medicines which draw out or correct the noxious blood. By little and little you have the advantage of spurring them up by emulation, which seldom fails. This in some measure I want. But whither am I carried ? Observing my little [illegible . . .] esteem for you, I suspect [=expect ?] my boy [?] to join with you in reading. Geordie readily will ; and you'll begin with Mr. Wood[1] when he comes over. I am very willing to join with you as far as opportunity answers.

May He who in all things gives the increase, cherish, ripen, and preserve you in your labours and studies.[2]

[DAVID ARNOT].

[1] Probably the once celebrated Edinburgh teacher of elocution, who was also manager of the theatre, and the friend of Fergusson.

[2] This letter was written in acknowledgement of " Daphnis : a Monody " on the death of young Arnot.

Chapter XI

THE WRITINGS OF BRUCE

We shall now endeavour to give some estimate of the works of Bruce and their promise of future excellence had their author lived, as in the case of his English contemporary, Cowper, to give us his mature productions. The poems of Michael Bruce do not appeal to the popular taste in the same way that those of Ramsay, Burns, Hogg, and many of our Scottish poets do, whose poems are invariably couched in the language of the dear old mother tongue, but they display a delicacy of thought and beautiful simplicity of language which have ever a charm for all readers, young and old alike, of a refined and cultivated taste. Many illustrious contributions have been made to English literature since Michael Bruce was laid in his untimely grave ; and amidst the brilliancy of these greater lights, his poetry, with the exception of two pieces which everybody knows, is apt to be unnoticed ; but just as many a lovely flower is all the more prized because it is found blooming in the shade, so his writings and history, although adorning only the by-paths of literature, will ever elicit the admiration and gratitude of those whose good fortune it is to alight upon them. If the effusions of a youth, who died so young, suffer in comparison with the elaborate performances of maturer years, the example of his life, singularly free from the blemishes that often tarnish the fame of men of genius, and beautified with the most unassuming piety, puts to shame the follies and vices of loftier names, and helps to light up the spiritual gloom of a period when religion was merely a sentiment—when the infidelity of the pulpit was scarcely concealed under a specious morality. Many affecting passages have indeed been written in his memory ; but it is the details of his life and the history of the productions themselves, as written by the affectionate pen of the late Dr. Mackelvie, that absorb our minds and stir our hearts with such contrary feelings. At one stage of the narrative we are melted into tenderness, at another, elevated to admiration. Here we are roused to indignation, and there we feel the liveliest gratitude. These efforts, moreover, are not produced by the arts of a special pleader or the tricks of eloquence, but by a plain statement of facts. After all, however, the intrinsic merit of Bruce's poems is of a very high order; and although, like many other admirable productions, they are comparatively neglected, yet in days when Blair, Ramsay, and Ferguson, Thomson, Beatie, and Home were reviving Scotland's literary fame—when Burns, Scott and Campbell were boys at school—the posthumous publication of some of these poems afforded delight to the literary clubs which gathered around such men as Henry Mackenzie and Lord Craig. To receive the praise of the men who met around the festive boards of Edinburgh to display their genius and retail literary gossip was certainly no mean distinction ; but still greater honour was conferred upon the poet when Lord Craig made him the subject of one of his papers in the *Mirror*, a periodical in which he, along with the " Man of Feeling " and other literati, reflected their gentle humour and cultivated taste upon the most interesting topics of the day. Lord Craig commended the poetry and gave the brief outlines of Michael Bruce's affecting life-story so touchingly as to render it worthy of being reprinted with almost every edition of Bruce's works. Here we would quote the closing paragraph of this interesting paper from the *Mirror* :—

" I have been led into these reflections from the persual of a small volume, which happens now to lie before me, which, though possessed of very considerable merit, and composed in this country, is, I believe, very little known. In a well written preface, the reader is told that most of them are the production of Michael Bruce ; that this Michael Bruce was born in a remote village in Kinross-shire, and descended from parents remarkable for nothing but the innocence and simplicity of their lives ; that in the 21st year of his age he was seized with a consumption, which put an end to his life. Nothing, methinks, has more the power of awakening benevolence than the consideration of genius thus de-pressed by situation, suffered to pine in obscurity, and sometimes, as in the case of this unfortunate young man, to perish, it may be, for want of those comforts and con-veniences which might have fostered a delicacy of frame or of mind, ill calculated to bear the hardships which poverty lays upon both. For my own part, I never pass the place (a little hamlet, skirted with a circle of old ash trees, about three miles from Kinross) where Michael resided ; I never look on his dwelling (a small thatched house, distin-guished from the cottages of the other inhabitants only by a sashed window at the end, instead of a lattice, fringed with a honeysuckle plant, which the poor youth had trained around it) ; I never find myself on that spot but I stop my horse involuntarily, and looking on the window which the honeysuckle has now almost covered, in the dream of the moment I picture out a figure for the gentle tenant of the mansion. I wish, and my heart swells while I do so, that he were alive, and that I were a great man, to have the luxury of visiting him there, and of bidding him be happy. I cannot carry my readers thither, but that they may share some of my feelings I will present them with an extract from the last poem in the little volume before me, which, from the subject and the manner in which it is written, cannot fail in touching the heart of every man who reads it."

The poem which Lord Craig refers to is the " Elegy in Spring." Later still, after the appearance of this article in the *Mirror*, when it became generally known that the Rev. John Logan had appropriated some of Bruce's finest pieces and suppressed his MS., we find Dr. Anderson, Principal Baird, Sir John Moore's father, Robert Burns, and many others, all contributing to undo the injury done to his fame, and mitigate the poverty of his aged mother. Again, in 1837, Dr. Mackelvie revived the interest previously taken in Bruce's fate by producing his elaborate memoir in which are detailed the minutest particulars of the poet's life, the question regarding the MS. being ably and impartially discussed. Further, in 1865, there was published a superbly illustrated edition of the Life and Poems of Michael Bruce, edited by Rev. Dr. Grosart All the editions, however, as we have already observed, are now out of print, and this is surely a happy indication of the wide-spread interest which the appearance of any volumes relating to Bruce invariably awakens.

The young poet was happy in his surroundings, as at every turn there was a view of the fair landscape of hill and dale, of river, lake, and woods, while his ear would be alive to all the music of rural life, including the sweet notes of the cuckoo. His poetry holds the same place in the literature of his country as the landscape presented by his native shire occupies among the scenes admired by all who are sensible to the attractions of nature, and of indescribable fascination to those who delight in associating the vicissitudes of humanity with the works of creation.

Child as he was, Michael Bruce must have shared early in the pleasure of those " circling round the fire " who listened to his worthy father describing scenes so suggestive of the sunshine and gloom of human life, and of the transient nature of all earthly glory. The gray towers of Falkland are silent ; but we still hear the sound of revelry alternating with the dying groans of the hapless Rothesay, and the heavy sighs of the broken-hearted James. The scene changes and the woods are vocal with the sounds of horn and hound ; and the gay courtiers ride forth to hunt the deer and fly the hawk. And shall Mary Queen of Scots be forgotten ?—the most beautiful, the most accomplished, the most unfortunate of an unfortunate race ! She too sought pleasure and retirement in Falkland—now threading the mazes of the Lomond woods—again reading Latin and Greek with Buchanan, or passing the time at music or chess. After a few bright days shame and confusion crowd upon her, and she is consigned to the gloom of Lochleven Castle. Thus would the tragic story be followed up. And would those boys hear nothing of Andrew Wynton ?—of St. Serf, and his ram of great renown ?—or of the ruined sanctuaries that once reflected their towers in the lake ? Yes ! they are transported back to other ages when superstition thronged Portmoak with Pilgrims from every quarter. Again in Covenanting times, in secluded dells among the Lomonds, they hear the subdued strains of the persecuted worshippers of God. Here, in the Lomond solitudes, is a projecting rock called the " Covenanter's Pulpit," where at various times, in years long gone by, have been heard the voices of the fearless Cameron, and of Blackadder, Wellwood, Welsh, and others, as they declared the whole counsel of God to assembled multitudes who eagerly listened in the natural amphitheatre opposite.

A solemn spot,
To solemn purposes 'twas dedicate
Of yore, " The Covenanter's Pulpit " named ;
There stood undaunted Cameron, his flock
Seated around and on the adverse banks,
Who listened grim to his wild eloquence ;
There wrestled he in spirit, and inspired
Enthusiastic awe in all who heard.

THE HOLLOW HILL OF GLENVALE

In such a glen as this, on such a day,
A poet might in solitude recline,
And while the hours unheeded stole away,
Gather rich fancies in the art divine.

The Retreat of the Covenanters. Here preached those of honoured name, Richard Cameron, Wellwood, Blackadder, Renwick, Cargill and others, to gather thousands from time to time, men who fought for the freedom of conscience and the glory of Jesus Christ.

POEM ON LOCHLEVEN

As a poetical description of the vale of Kinross, and an accurate topographical account of its localities, the poem is all that could be desired. The poem was written when Michael Bruce was at Forest Mill.

> Mildly soft the western breeze
> Just kissed the lake, just stirred the trees ;
> And the pleased lake, like maiden coy,
> Trembled, but dimpled not for joy.

Lochleven Castle is described, but there is no allusion to the fair prisoner, Mary Queen of Scots, who was once imprisoned there. Here was a poetical romance in itself, which the fancy of any poet could have revelled in, but Bruce pays no attention to it. We agree with Dr. Mackelvie that " interesting as the poem of ' Lochleven ' is, it would have been still more so had the imprisonment of Mary in its castle been the subject, and the description of its scenery a part of its illustration and embellishment. This plan might have been pursued under the same title with even more propriety than the one adopted." The true reason, however, for not mentioning Queen Mary we think Mr. Mackenzie gives in stating that the sufferings inflicted upon loyal and noble Christian Scotsmen of all ranks during the reign of Charles the Second were well known to all who resided in the district. Charles was the great-grandson of Queen Mary, and numerous were the tales of war and woe that were poured into the ears of the young people around the local firesides of the Bishopshire. Even Mary herself had left behind her in this locality no very good name. All this was familiar to the young poet, and while it is possible that Bruce would have been inclined to justify the queen to a great extent, he felt he could not so do in the measure likely to please her admirers. In view of his desire to become a minister of the Secession Church, he had to consider the feelings of his more immediate friends. The introduction of her name might have been misunderstood. His wisdom, therefore, is seen in leaving out all reference to Queen Mary.

Bruce excels in describing the scenery, as for instance what could be finer or more accurate in its details than the following description ? :—

> The twilight trembles o'er the misty hills,
> Trinkling with dews ; and whilst the bird of day
> Tunes his ethereal note and wakes the wood,
> Bright from the crimson curtains of the morn,
> The sun appearing in his glory throws
> New robes of beauty over heav'n and earth.
> O now, while Nature smiles in all her works,
> Oft let me trace thy cowslip-cover'd banks,
> O Leven ! and the landscape measure round,
> From gay Kinross, whose stately tufted groves
> Nod o'er the lake, transported let mine eye
> Wander o'er all the various chequer'd scene,
> Of wilds, and fertile fields, and glitt'ring streams,
> To ruin'd Arnot ; or ascend the height
> Of rocky Lomond, where a riv'let pure
> Bursts from the ground, and through the crumbled crags
> Tinkles amusive. From the mountain's top,
> Around me spread I see the goodly scene !

The general excellence of this poem may be judged from the fact, that Campbell in his " Specimens of the English Poets," Drake in his " Literary Hours," Chambers in his " Biographical Dictionary of Eminent Scotsmen," and Forsyth in his " Beauties of Scotland," have each quoted different portions of it as beautiful passages, and in this way have nearly divided the whole poem

amongst them. Dr. Anderson says concerning it :—" His
' Lochleven ' is the longest and most elaborate of his
poetical compositions. It is a descriptive poem written
in blank verse, the structure of which he seems to have
particularly studied, as it exhibits a specimen of considerable strength and harmony in that measure. Though
the nature of the subject approaches nearly to that of
Thomson, of whom he was a great admirer, his style is
very different, being wholly free from that unnatural
swell and pomp of words, which too often disfigure the
beautiful descriptions of Thomson. It represents an
extensive and beautiful prospect in an animated and
pleasing manner. It has much appropriate description and
picturesque imagery ; and it is rendered interesting by
poetical fictions, historical allusions, and moral reflections.
But it is not without defects ; there is a redundance of
thought in some instances, and a carelessness of language
in others. He has, however, availed himself of every
circumstance that could with propriety be introduced
to decorate his poem. The story of Lomond and Levina
is happily introduced and simply and pleasingly related.
The picture of ' the man of sorrows new risen from the
bed of pain ' is natural and striking. Lochleven Castle,
the Inch, the Limestone Quarries, and the rivers Po, Queech
Leven and Gairney, ' on whose banks he first tuned the
Doric reed,' are graphically and poetically described.
The compliment to Laelius is a pleasing digression, and
the description of the character and dwelling of Agricola,
towards the conclusion, has great merit. The poem is
local ; and though local description is far more adapted
to the pencil than the pen, yet it will be perused with
delight by poetical lovers of rural imagery, and must
be peculiarly pleasing to those who are familiar with
the picturesque scenery of Lochleven."

It is somewhat singular that the poet gives little consideration to the lake itself or to the various aspects

in which it presents itself at sunrise or sunset, with all the beautiful effects of light and shade produced by fickle nature. Even in Autumn, when there is a little ripple on the lake, and the sun at break of day is peeping over Benarty, what a charming effect is produced.

The Kinross-shire hills dwindle into insignificance when compared with the gigantic ranges of other counties. The prospects are not so commanding, the confusion so sublime, the floods so magnificent, nor the tempests so terrific. Again, Lochleven—evermore a theme of praise to those who can boast of having been nursed on its shores, and the chief attraction Kinross offers to tourists and anglers—presents not the grandeur which characterises some of the Highland lakes; its surface is not so extensive, its islets so numerous nor so diversified ; nor does it reflect forests so dense or mansions so splendid ; but its historical and romantic associations are none the less interesting.

If the votary of Nature must go elsewhere for sublimer scenes or more luscious exuberance, *here* he will delight in her softer touches and more beautiful combinations. He will roam over verdant hills and flowery dales— he will thread the mazes of silvery streams, whose waters descend in gentle murmurs to the lake below—his eye will linger with delight on the pleasant abodes of the Agricolas of the plain, and his ear be regaled with the warblings of ten thousand voices ! Still more famous are the scenes for the associations which history and tradition throw around them ; and how often is the loiterer away among the Lomonds and the Ochils lost in the memories of the past, fancy and feeling uniting with fact to paint to the mind of the enthusiast those events which will ever make Lochleven and its environment memorable—events that give Kinross a fame which many sublimer scenes do not possess !

Similar have been the ideas and emotions we have experienced in comparing Michael Bruce's works with those which have been written on kindred subjects. In reading his poetry you do not feel overpowered by the sublimity of Milton, awed by the gloom of Blair, or repulsed by the horrors of Pollock ; nor, on the other hand, are you satiated with the luxurious imagery of Thomson. But just as these will strike the attentive reader as prominent features of the authors so named, so will it be found that, whilst none of these characteristics are absent from Bruce's poems, in them simplicity of thought and beauty of language everywhere abound ; and that, at agreeable intervals, pathos and humour give place to one another. Lastly, to complete the figure, these writings, read in connection with the incidents of the author's life and their own history, awaken emotions, lead to reflections, and connect themselves with names which increase their interest and enhance their value. This will be the verdict of every native of Kinross-shire who studies the life and writings of Bruce in a calm, intelligent spirit. In his life-time Bruce wrote a good deal, considering his circumstances.

"In estimating the position of Michael Bruce," observes Dr. Grosart, "among the minor poets of our country, three things must be remembered. (1) That the ' Ode to the Cuckoo ' and the ' Hymns,' being proven to be his, we have in them a token of what, had years been given him, he might and would have done. (2) That the quarto volume into which he had transcribed all his poems under the shadow of departure, was *destroyed* by Logan. It probably contained many such gems as those named. I strongly suspect that the ballad of the ' Braes of Yarrow,' and the Tale commencing, ' Where pastoral Tweed, renown'd in song,' were, in substance, from his Muse, not Logan's. (3) That he died only three months beyond his twenty-first year. This explains the immaturity of his tastes, and his echoes of Milton and Thomson, Gray and Collins, Young and other poets.

But as it is, this volume of the ' Works ' of our poet deserves a place among the genuine ' *Makkars.*' Even in his barest productions, as ' Lochleven ' and ' The Last Day,' there are bits of description not at all unworthy of the master, Thomson."

Probably Bruce's poems did not command much popularity at their first publication. Their beauties are such as appeal to minds which can appreciate " delicacy of thought and beautiful simplicity of language, qualities which do not commend themselves to the multitude." Dr. Anderson, who, upon the whole, has formed a very correct estimate of the merits of Bruce's poems, says : " As a poet, Bruce is characterized by elegance, simplicity and tenderness, more than sublimity, invention, or enthusiasm. He has more judgment and feeling than genius or imagination. He is an elegant and pleasing, though not a very animated nor original writer. His compositions are the production of a tender fancy, a cultivated taste, and a benevolent mind ; and are distinguished by an amiable delicacy and simplicity of sentiment, and a graceful plainness of expression, free from the affectation of an inflated diction, and a profusion of imagery, so common in juvenile productions. His thoughts are often striking, sometimes new, and always just ; and his versification, though not exquisitely polished, is commonly easy and harmonious. His ' Elegy Written in Spring,' is characterized by energy, simplicity, pathos and melody, in the highest degree. From the circumstances in which it was written, the nature of its subject, and the merit of its execution, it has obtained an uncommon share of popularity. The influences and effects of Spring are expressed by a selection of such imagery as is adapted to strike the imagination by lively pictures. The manner in which he describes its effects upon himself is so pathetically circumstantial, and so universally interesting, that it powerfully awakens all our tenderness :

> ——but not to me returns
> The vernal joy my better years have known ;
> Dim in my breast life's dying taper burns,
> And all the joys of life with health are flown.

It is unnecessary to refer to Bruce's works in detail. His sacred poems have been a source of comfort and refreshment to many in trying circumstances. Lines of these hymns are met with, carved on tombstones, far and near. Sympathy is the soul of all goodness, and thus has Bruce represented the Son of God to us in one of his paraphrases in such simple words of love and encouragement as these :—

> Tho' now ascended up on high,
> He bends on earth a brother's eye,
> Partaker of the human name,
> He knows the frailty of our frame.

If we take Hymn v, of the five Hymns appended to the " Translations and Paraphrases " of the Bible, with which we are all more or less familiar, we cannot but feel how it breathes the very spirit of our young dying poet.

> I leave the world without a tear,
> Save for the friends I hold so dear ;
> To heal their sorrows, Lord, descend,
> And to the friendless prove a friend.
>
> I come, I come, at Thy command,
> I give my spirit to Thine hand ;
> Stretch forth Thine everlasting arms,
> And shield me in the last alarms.
>
> The hour of my departure's come.
> I hear the voice that calls me home ;
> Now, O my God ! let trouble cease ;
> Now let Thy servant die in peace.

H

In " Sir James the Ross," an historical ballad, Bruce displays the versatility of his genius. " Whether we consider," remarks Dr. Anderson, " the beautiful simplicity of the story, the delicacy of its situations, the pathos of its discoveries, the exact delineation of the manners of the times to which it refers, the genuine strokes of nature and of passion, or the unremitting animation of the whole, we cannot but highly admire the mixture it exhibits of genius and of art. The story on which it is founded, though romantic, is interesting, and the more so, as there is reason to believe it is in some measure authentic. It is a tale of tenderness and distress ; and challenges a place with the ' Hardy-knute ' of his countryman, Sir John Bruce of Kinross, the ' Owen of Carron ' of Langhorne, and other successful imitations of the ancient historical ballad." This interesting ballad of " Sir James the Ross," which Bruce wrote in one evening, consists of over fifty stanzas.

Reference has already been made to the poems of " The Last Day," " Lochleven," and " Elegy in Spring." Leaving Bruce's ludicrous pieces, the " Musiad " and " Anacreontic to a Wasp," which are not void of humour and pleasantry, and his songs which are tender and easy, we pass on to the consideration of his immortal " Ode to the Cuckoo," which, every time it is repeated, falls as sweetly upon our ears as the cunning notes of the bird in Spring to which it is addressed.

The cuckoo has been the theme of many poets, but Bruce's ode will scarcely be excelled for its natural freshness, simple grace, and delicate description. It was the first of Bruce's poems we committed to memory. The poem will always suggest pleasant memories to the mind on which it is photographed. Meeting an art critic in London on one occasion—a thorough-going Scot—he began repeating the " Ode to the Cuckoo " on hearing we came from Kinross-shire. We helped him through some verses he had difficulty in recalling. Twice he asked us to repeat that verse—

> Sweet bird ! thy bower is ever green,
>   Thy sky is ever clear,
> Thou hast no sorrow in thy song,
>   No winter in thy year !.

Then repeating the verse to us he said, " I have got it off by heart now, and it will be something to refresh my spirit, as I think of it, when I am walking along Fleet Street, where I have to go now." Not this verse only, but the entire poem is very refreshing indeed. To Logan's credit be it said he warmly eulogised the poet in the original edition of his poems which he published. " If images of nature," says Logan, " beautiful and new ; if sentiments, warm from the heart, interesting and pathetic ; if a style, chaste with ornament, and elegant with simplicity ; if these and many other beauties of nature and art are allowed to constitute the true poetic merit, these poems will stand high in the judgment of men of taste." In conclusion, while there are no religious poets in Scotland to be placed side by side with Ramsay, Burns, and Scott, Michael Bruce is more than a mere hymn writer. He is recognised as one of the minor poets of Scotland, whose writings are of commanding interest, breathing the spirit of sincere piety and unmistakable genius. Moreover his " Scripture Sonnets " are described as the best known and the most admired of our Scottish paraphrases. Michael Bruce, so amiable, kindly, and gentle in his disposition, so generous and unostentatious, has left behind him a name which base injustice has long deprived of much of its fame, but which even at this distant day will acquire additional lustre and renown.

Referring to the many tributes paid to the genius of Michael Bruce, the poet of Lochleven, the following letter from Robert Burns is worthy of record. It was written in reply to a request by Dr. Baird on 8th February, 1791, soliciting the aid of our national poet in a scheme which involved the publication of the poems of Bruce for the benefit of his mother, who was then " a woman of eighty years of age, poor and helpless." The writer recalls the " honourable tribute paid to a kindred genius in Ferguson, and fondly hopes that the mother of Bruce would experience his patronage." The response of Burns is characteristic of the affectionate regard which he felt for his highly gifted brother poet : —
" Why did you, my dear Sir, write to me in such a hesitating style on the business ? Have I not felt the many ills that poetic flesh is heir to ? You shall have your choice of all the unpublished poems I have, and had your letter had my direction, so as to have reached me sooner (it only came to my hands this moment) I should directly put you out of suspense upon the subject. I only ask that some prefatory advertisement in the book may bear that the publication is solely for the benefit of the mother. I would not put it in the power of ignorance to surmise, or malice to insinuate, that I clubbed a share of the merit from mercenary motives. Nor need you give me credit for any remarkable generosity in my part of the business. I have such a host of peccadilloes, failings, follies, and backslidings (anyone but myself would perhaps give them a worse appellation) that by the way of some balance, however trifling, in the account, I am fain to do any good that occurs in my very limited power to a fellow-creature, just from the selfish purpose of clearing a little the vista of retrospection."

Referring to the above, Mr. J. Birrell addressed a letter to the Rev. G. Baird, Dunkeld, 13th February, 1792, from which we quote :—

" Being much interested in the old woman's welfare and in the success of the intended publication, as well as for the satisfaction of several friends, permit me to say regarding the admission of Mr. Burns's pieces, the dissimilarity between Mr. Burns's poems and the innocent simplicity and moral tendency of Mr. Bruce's poetry is very striking."

The pieces promised by Burns did not ultimately appear in Dr. Baird's edition of Bruce's Poems. It may be interesting here to observe that Bruce's Poems were valued and praised by the two greatest poets who immediately succeeded him—viz. Robert Fergusson and his successor, Robert Burns, who embodied Michael Bruce's sentiments in two of his grandest pieces, " The Cotter's Saturday Night " and Bruce's address to his army at Bannockburn, " Scots wha hae."

Bruce writes :

Thou guardian angel of Britannia's Isle.

Burns puts this as :

And stand a wall of fire around our much loved Isle.

Bruce writes :

Thy sons shall lay the proud oppressor low.

Burns adopts this in his " Scots wha hae : "

Lay the proud usurper low.

Bruce in his " Elegy in Spring," writes :

Taught them to sing the great Creator's praise.

Burns in his " Cotter's Saturday Night," has :

Together hymning their Creator's praise.

Bruce in his " Loch Leven," writes :

> My one beloved, were the Scottish throne
> To me transmitted thro' a scepter'd line
> Of ancestors, thou should'st be my queen,
> And Caledonia's diadem adorn
> A fairer head than ever wore a crown.

Burns reflects this in " Oh, wert thou in the cauld blast " :

> Or were I monarch of the globe,
> Wi' thee to reign, wi' thee to reign,
> The brightest jewel in my crown
> Wad be my queen, wad be my queen.

" THE WOOD "
To which so many references are made in Bruce's writings

THE WORKS OF MICHAEL BRUCE

ODE TO THE CUCKOO

HAIL, beauteous Stranger of the wood !
    Attendant on the Spring !
Now heav'n repairs thy rural seat,
    And woods thy welcome sing.

Soon as the daisy decks the green,
    Thy certain voice we hear :
Hast thou a star to guide thy path,
    Or mark the rolling year ?

Delightful visitant ! with thee
    I hail the time of flow'rs,
When heav'n is fill'd with music sweet
    Of birds among the bow'rs.

The schoolboy wand'ring in the wood
    To pull the flow'rs so gay,
Starts, thy curious voice to hear,
    And imitates thy lay.

Soon as the pea puts on the bloom
    Thou fly'st thy vocal vale,
An annual guest, in other lands,
    Another spring to hail.

Sweet bird ! thy bow'r is ever green.
　　Thy sky is ever clear ;
Thou hast no sorrow in thy song.
　　No winter in thy year !

Alas ! sweet bird ! not so my fate,
　　Dark scowling skies I see
Fast gathering round, and fraught with woe
　　And wintry years to me.

O could I fly, I'd fly with thee :
　　We'd make, with social wing,
Our annual visit o'er the globe,
　　Companions of the Spring.

THE CUCKOO

ELEGY WRITTEN IN SPRING

This poem has been much admired, and was early noticed by Lord Craig (see p. 88). The scene before the poet's mind is taken from his usual standpoint, " the Wood," overlooking the parish church. In the distance is the site of the old kirk, where his dear friend, " Willie Arnot," was buried, and where he desires to be laid to " rest in the hope of an eternal day." This is believed to have been the last poem Bruce wrote.

'Tis past : the iron North has spent his rage ;
    Stern Winter now resigns the length'ning day ;
The stormy howlings of the winds assuage,
    And warm o'er ether western breezes play.

Of genial heat and cheerful light the source,
    From southern climes, beneath another sky,
The sun, returning, wheels his golden course ;
    Before his beams all noxious vapours fly.

Far to the north grim Winter draws his train
    To his own clime, to Zembla's frozen shore ;
Where, thron'd on ice, he holds eternal reign ;
    Where whirlwinds madden, and where tempests roar.

Loos'd from the bands of frost, the verdant ground
    Again puts on her robe of cheerful green,
Again puts forth her flow'rs ; and all around,
    Smiling, the cheerful face of Spring is seen.

Behold ! the trees new-deck their wither'd boughs ;
    Their ample leaves the hospitable plane,
The taper elm, and lofty ash, disclose ;
    The blooming hawthorn variegates the scene.

The lily of the vale, of flow'rs the Queen,
   Puts on the robe she neither sew'd nor spun ;
The birds on ground, or on the branches green,
   Hop to and fro, and glitter in the sun.

Soon as o'er eastern hills the morning peers,
   From her low nest the tufted lark upsprings ;
And, cheerful singing, up the air she steers ;
   Still high she mounts, still loud and sweet she sings.

On the green furze, cloth'd o'er with golden blooms
   That fill the air with fragrance all around,
The linnet sits, and tricks his glossy plumes,
   While o'er the wild his broken notes resound.

While the sun journeys down the western sky,
   Along the greensward, mark'd with Roman mound,
Beneath the blithesome shepherd's watchful eye,
   The cheerful lambkins dance and frisk around.

Now is the time for those who wisdom love,
   Who love to walk in Virtue's flow'ry road,
Along the lovely paths of Spring to rove,
   And follow " Nature up to Nature's God."[1]

The Zoroasters studied Nature's laws ;
   Thus Socrates, the wisest of mankind ;
Thus heav'n-taught Plato trac'd th' Almighty cause,
   And left the wondr'ing multitude behind.

[1] " *And follow up to Nature's God.*" Pope had said :
      Slave to no sect, who takes no private road,
      But looks thro' Nature up to Nature's God.
                      " Essay on Man."

THE POET SETTING OUT ON HIS FAVOURITE WALK ', TO THE WOOD ''
The Fairies' Knowe on the left
'' There oft he walked along the dewy lawn ''

Thus Ashley gather'd Academic bays ;
  Thus gentle Thomson, as the Seasons roll,
Taught them to sing the great Creator's praise,
  And bear their poet's name from pole to pole.

Thus have I walk'd along the dewy lawn ;
  My frequent foot the blooming wild hath worn ;
Before the lark I've sung the beauteous dawn,
  And gather'd health from all the gales of morn.

And, even when Winter chill'd the aged year,
  I wander'd lonely o'er the hoary plain ;
Tho' frosty Boreas warn'd me to forbear,
  Boreas, with all his tempests, warn'd in vain.

Then, sleep my nights, and quiet bless'd my days ;
  I fear'd no loss, my mind was all my store ;
No anxious wishes e'er disturb'd my ease ;
  Heav'n gave content and health—I ask'd no more.

Now Spring returns : but not to me returns
  The vernal joy my better years have known ;
Dim in my breast life's dying taper burns,
  And all the joys of life with health are flown.

Starting and shiv'ring in th' constant wind,
  Meagre and pale, the ghost of what I was,
Beneath some blasted tree I lie reclin'd,
  And count the silent moments as they pass :

The winged moments, whose unstaying speed
  No art can stop, or in their course arrest ;
Whose flight shall shortly count me with the dead,
  And lay me down in peace with them that rest.

Oft morning-dreams presage approaching fate ;
   And morning-dreams, as poets tell, are true.
Led by pale ghosts, I enter Death's dark gate,
   And bid the realms of light and life adieu.

I hear the helpless wail, the shriek of woe ;
   I see the muddy wave, the dreary shore,
The sluggish streams that slowly creep below,
   Which mortals visit, and return no more.

Farewell, ye blooming fields ! ye cheerful plains !
   Enough for me the churchyard's lonely mound,
Where Melancholy with still Silence reigns,
   And the rank grass waves o'er the cheerless ground.

There let me wander at the shut of eve,
   When sleep sits dewy on the labourer's eyes,
The world and all its busy follies leave,
   And talk with Wisdom where my Daphnis lies.

There let me sleep forgotten in the clay,
   When death shall shut these weary aching eyes ;
Rest in the hopes of an eternal day,
   Till the long night's gone, and the last morn arise.

LOCHLEVEN

Lochleven, the subject of Bruce's longest poem, lies towards the east end of the vale of Kinross. To the south and east runs the ridge of the Lomonds. The traces of the landslip on the sides of Benarty give an abrupt and rugged appearance to the southern setting. Further eastward and northward rise the " rocky Lomonds," on whose verdant slopes the young poet first revelled in the quiet beauty of the panorama, of which he was afterwards so nobly to essay the description.

It is now well-nigh 160 years since Bruce laid the scene of his most elaborate descriptive poem, with true poetic instinct, in his own native vale, with its embosomed lake, so replete with stirring memories, both ancient and modern. Since that time, while the main features of this classic region have remained the same, both the aspect of the loch and its surroundings have changed. The castle on its island is here, as of old, with its square tower and rampart, its memories of great political movements, of distinguished inmates, especially of Mary Stuart. St. Serf's has still the ruins of its ancient priory, the traces of its monastery, and its Culdee burying-ground. But even these islands have grown in size since Bruce looked down upon them from the slopes of Bishop Hill, and other smaller islets have lifted up their heads.

By the drainage of the loch in 1830, its area was reduced from 4638 imperial acres to somewhat over 3000 ; thus exposing, in and around it, a new margin of soil, on which, here and there, adding a fresh charm to the scene, are groves of spruce and pine planted by the Laird of Lochleven.

We do not speak here of the unique interest which belongs to Lochleven from the angler's point of view, except simply to remark that Lochleven trout are everywhere famous for their excellent flavour and bright colour. We have said enough, we trust, to make it clear that in historical and literary interest of every description, from Wyntoun's " Cronykil of Scotland " on to Bruce's Poems and Sir Walter Scott's " Abbot," Lochleven may well claim a foremost place among Scottish lakes, and may well have its own native poet.

LOCHLEVEN WITH THE CASTLE ON ISLAND

From Photo by Mr. Gardiner, Milnathort.

III

LOCHLEVEN

Hail, native land ! where on the flow'ry banks
Of Leven, Beauty ever-blooming dwells ;
A wreath of roses, dropping with the dews
Of Morning, circles her ambrosial locks
Loose-waving o'er her shoulders ; where she treads,
Attendant on her steps, the blushing Spring
And Summer wait, to raise the various flowr's
Beneath her footsteps ; while the cheerful birds
Carol their joy, and hail her as she comes,
Inspiring vernal love and vernal joy.
　　Attend, Agricola ![1] who to the noise
Of public life preferr'st the calmer scenes
Of solitude, and sweet domestic bliss,
Joys all thine own ! attend thy poet's strain,
Who triumphs in thy friendship, while he paints,
The past'ral mountains, the poetic streams,
Where raptur'd Contemplation leads thy walk,
While silent Evening on the plain descends.
　　Between two mountains, whose o'erwhelming tops,
In their swift course, arrest the bellying clouds,
A pleasant valley lies. Upon the south,
A narrow op'ning parts the craggy hills ;
Through which the loch, that beautifies the vale,
Pours out its ample waters. Spreading on,
And wid'ning by degrees, it stretches north
To the high Ochil, from whose snowy top
The streams that feed the loch flow thund'ring down.

---

[1] Mr. David Arnot, the laird of Portmoak and the poet's valued
friend, at whose instance this poem was written.

LOCHLEVEN

The twilight trembles o'er the misty hills,
Trinkling with dews ; and whilst the bird of day
Tunes his ethereal note, and wakes the wood,
Bright from the crimson curtains of the morn,
The sun appearing in his glory, throws
New robes of beauty over heav'n and earth.
 O now, while Nature smiles in all her works,
Oft let me trace thy flower-cover'd banks,
O Leven ! and the landscape measure round.
From gay Kinross, whose stately tufted groves
Nod o'er the loch, transported let mine eye
Wander o'er all the various chequer'd scene,
Of wilds and fertile fields, and glittering streams,
To ruin'd Arnot[1] ; or ascend the height
Of rocky Lomond, where a riv'let pure[2]
Bursts from the ground, and through
        the crumbled crags
Tinkles amusive. From the mountain's top,
Around me spread, I see the goodly scene !
Inclosures green, that promise to the swain
The future harvest ; many-colour'd meads ;
Irriguous vales, where cattle low, and sheep
That whiten half the hills ; sweet rural farms
Oft interspers'd, the seats of past'ral love
And innocence ; with many a spiry dome
Sacred to heav'n, around whose hallow'd walls
Our fathers slumber in the narrow house.

[1] The ruins of a castle, a stronghold of the Arnots, once of great
size and strength, on the Lomond Hills, at the eastern extremity of
Lochleven, as Kinross is at the western. Kinross and Arnot are mentioned
by the poet to define the limits of the scene he intends to describe.
In William III.'s first parliament, Sir David Arnot represented the shire
of Kinross.

[2] This stream in its course to Lochleven is frequently mentioned
in other poems.

Gay beauteous villas, bosom'd in the woods,
Like constellations in the starry sky,
Complete the scene. The vales, the vocal hills.
The woods, the waters, and the heart of man
Send out a gen'ral song ; 'tis beauty all
To poet's eye and music to his ear.
   Nor is the shepherd silent on his hill,
His flocks around ; nor schoolboys, as they creep,
Slow pac'd, tow'rd school ; intent, with oaten pipe
They wake by turns wild music on the way.
   Behold the man of sorrows hail the light !
New risen from the bed of pain, where late,
Toss'd to and fro upon a couch of thorns,
He wak'd the long dark night, and wish'd for morn.
Soon as he feels the quick'ning beam of heav'n,
And balmy breath of May, among the fields
And flow'rs he takes his morning walk : his heart
Beats with new life ; his eye is bright and blithe ;
Health strews her roses o'er his cheek ; renew'd
In youth and beauty, his unbidden tongue
Pours native harmony, and sings to heav'n.
   In ancient times as ancient Bards have sung,
This was a forest.[1] Here the mountain-oak
Hung o'er the craggy cliff, while from its top
The eagle mark'd his prey ; the stately ash
Rear'd high his nervous stature, while below
The twining alders darken'd all the scene.
Safe in the shade, the tenants of the wood
Assembled, bird and beast. The turtle-dove
Coo'd amorous all the livelong summer's day.
Lover of men, the piteous redbreast plain'd,
Sole-sitting on the bough. Blithe on the bush
The blackbird, sweetest of the woodland choir
Warbled his liquid lay : to shepherd swain

---

[1] The " King-his-wood " was the old name.

Mellifluous music, as his master's flock,
With his fair mistress and his faithful dog,
He tended in the vale ; while leverets round,
In sportive races, through the forest flew
With feet of wind ; and, vent'ring from the rock,
The snow-white coney sought his evening meal.
Here, too, the poet, as inspir'd at eve
He roam'd the dusky wood, or fabled brook
That piece-meal printed ruins in the rock,
Beheld the blue-eyed Sisters of the stream,
And heard the wild note of the fairy throng
That charm'd the Queen of heav'n as round the tree
Time-hallo'd, hand in hand they led the dance,
With sky-blue mantles glitt'ring in her beam.

Low by the Loch, as yet without a name.
Fair bosom'd in the bottom of the vale,
Arose a cottage, green with ancient turf,
Half hid in hoary trees, and from the north
Fenc'd by a wood, but open to the sun.
Here dwelt a peasant, rev'rend with the locks
Of age, yet youth was ruddy on his cheek :
His farm his only care ; his sole delight
To tend his daughter, beautiful and young,
To watch her paths, to fill her lap with flow'rs,
To see her spread into the bloom of years,
The perfect picture of her mother's youth.
His age's hope, the apple of his eye ;
Belov'd of Heav'n, his fair Levina grew
In youth and grace, the Naiad of the Vale.
Fresh as the flow'r amid the sunny show'rs
Of May, and blither than the bird of dawn,
But roses' bloom gave beauty to her cheek
Soft-temper'd with a smile. The light of heav'n
And innocence illum'd her virgin-eye,
Lucid and lovely as the morning star.

Her breast was fairer than the vernal bloom
Of valley-lily, op'ning in a show'r
Fair as the morn, and beautiful as May,
The glory of the year, when first she comes
Array'd, all-beauteous, with the robes of heav'n,
And breathing summer breezes ; from her locks
Shakes genial dews, and from her lap the flow'rs.
Thus beautiful she look'd ; yet something more,
And better far than beauty, in her looks
Appear'd : the maiden blush of modesty ;
The smile of cheerfulness, and sweet content ;
Health's freshest rose, the sunshine of the soul ;
Each height'ning each, effus'd o'er all her form
A nameless grace, the beauty of her mind.
   Thus finish'd fair above her peers, she drew
The eyes of all the village, and inflam'd
The rival shepherds of the neighb'ring dale,
Who laid the spoils of Summer at her feet,
And made the woods enamour'd of her name,
But pure as buds before they blow, and still
A virgin in her heart, she knew not love ;
But all alone, amid her garden fair,
" From morn to noon, from noon to dewy eve,"[1]
She spent her days ; her pleasing task to tend
The flowr's ; to lave them from the water-spring ;
To ope the buds with her enamour'd breath,
Rank the gay tribes, and rear them in the sun.
In youth the index of maturer years,
Left by her school-companions at their play,
She'd often wander in the wood or roam
The wilderness, in quest of curious flow'r,
Or nest of bird unknown, till eve approach'd,
And hemm'd her in the shade. To obvious swain
Or woodman chanting in the greenwood glen,
She'd bring the beauteous spoils, and ask their names.

[1] Milton. P. L., Book I., p. 543.—G.

Thus ply'd assiduous her delightful task,
Day after day, till ev'ry herb she nam'd
That paints the robe of spring, and knew the voice
Of every warbler in the vernal wood.
    Her garden stretch'd along the river-side,
High up a sunny bank : on either side,
A hedge forbade the vagrant foot ; above,
An ancient forest screen'd the green recess.
Transplanted here by her creative hand,
Each herb of Nature, full of fragrant sweets,
That scents the breath of summer ; every flow'r,
Pride of the plain, that blooms on festal days
In shepherd's garland, and adorns the year.
In beauteous clusters flourish'd ; Nature's work,
And order, finish'd by the hand of Art.
Here gowans, natives of the village green,
To daisies grew. The lilies of the field
Put on the robe they neither sew'd nor spun.
Sweet-smelling shrubs and cheerful spreading trees,
Unfrequent scatter'd, as by Nature's hand,
Shaded the flow'rs, and to her Eden drew
The earliest concerts of the Spring, and all
The various music of the vocal year :
Retreat romantic ! Thus from early youth
Her life she led ; one summer's day, serene
And fair, without a cloud : like poet's dream
Of vernal landscapes, of Elysian vales,
And islands of the blest ; where, hand in hand,
Eternal Spring and Autumn rule the year,
And Love and Joy lead on immortal youth.
    'Twas on a summer's day, when early show'rs
Had wak'd the various vegetable race
To life and beauty, fair Levina stray'd.
Far in the blooming wilderness she stray'd
To gather herbs, and the fair race of flow'rs,

That Nature's hand creative pours at will,
Beauty unbounded ! over Earth's green lap,
Gay without number, in the day of rain.
O'er valleys gay, o'er hillocks green she walk'd
Sweet as the season, and at times awak'd
The echoes of the vale, with native notes
Of heart-felt joy in numbers heav'nly sweet ;
Sweet as th' hosannas of a Form of light,
A sweet-tongu'd Seraph in the bow'rs of bliss.
    Here, as she halted on a green hill-top,
A quiver'd hunter spied.   Her flowing locks,
In golden ringlets glittering to the sun,
Upon her bosom played :   her mantle green,
Like thine, O Nature ! to her rosy cheek
Lent beauty new ;   as from the verdant leaf
The rose-bud blushes with a deeper bloom,
Amid the walks of May.   The stranger's eye
Was caught as with ethereal presence.   Oft
He look'd to heav'n, and oft he met her eye
In all the silent eloquence of love ;
Then, waked from wonder, with a smile began :
" Fair wanderer of the wood ! What heav'nly
    Power,
Or Providence, conducts thy wandering steps
To this wild forest, from thy native seat
And parents, happy in a child so fair ?
A shepherdess, or virgin of the vale,
Thy dress bespeaks ; but thy majestic mien,
And eye, bright as the morning-star, confess
Superior birth and beauty, born to rule :
As from the stormy cloud of night, that veils
Her virgin-orb, appears the Queen of heaven
And with full beauty, gilds the face of night,
Whom shall I call the fairest of her sex,
And charmer of my soul ?   In yonder vale,
Come, let us crop the roses of the brook,

And wildings of the wood : Soft under shade
Let us recline by mossy fountain-side,
While the wood suffers in the beam of noon.
I'll bring my love the choice of all the shades ;
First fruits ; the apple ruddy from the stock ;
And clustering nuts, that burnish on the stem.
Wilt thou bless my dwelling, and become
The owner of these fields ? I'll give thee all
That I possess, and all thou seest is mine."
   Thus spoke the youth, with rapture in his eye,
And thus the maiden, with a blush began :
" Beyond the shadow of these mountains green,
Deep-bosom'd in the vale, a cottage stands.
The dwelling of my sire, a peaceful swain ;
Yet at his frugal board Health sits a guest,
And fair Contentment crowns his hoary hairs.
The patriarch of the plains : ne'er by his door
The needy passed, or the way-faring man.
His only daughter, and his only joy,
I feed my father's flock ; and, while they rest,
At times retiring, lose me in the wood,
Skill'd in the virtues of each secret herb
That opes its virgin bosom to the Moon.
No flow'r amid the garden fairer grows
Than the sweet lily of the lowly vale,
The Queen of flow'rs ; but sooner might the weed
That blooms and dies, the being of a day,
Presume to match with yonder mountain oak,
That stands the tempest and the bolt of Heaven,
From age to age the monarch of the wood—
O ! had you been a shepherd of the dale,
To feed your flock beside me, and to rest
With me at noon in these delightful shades,
I might have list'ned to the voice of love,
Nothing reluctant ; might with you have walked

Whole summer-suns away. At even-tide,
When heav'n and earth in all their glory shine
With the last smiles of the departing sun ;
When the sweet breath of Summer feasts the sense,
And secret pleasure thrills the heart of man ;
We might have walked alone, in converse sweet,
Along the quiet vale, and woo'd the Moon
To hear the music of true lovers' vows.
But fate forbids, and fortune's potent frown,
And honour, inmate of the noble breast.
Ne'er can this hand in wedlock join with thine.
Cease, beauteous stranger ! cease, beloved youth !
To vex a heart that never can be yours."
    Thus spoke the maid, deceitful : but her eyes
Beyond the partial purpose of her tongue,
Persuasion gain'd. The deep-enamoured youth
Stood gazing on her charms, and all his soul
Was lost in love. He grasped her trembling hand,
And breathed the softest, the sincerest vows
Of love : " O virgin ! fairest of the fair !
My one beloved ! Were the Scottish throne [1]
To me transmitted thro' a sceptr'd line
Of ancestors, thou, thou should'st be my Queen,
And Caledonia's diadem adorn
A fairer head than ever wore a crown."
She redden'd like the morning, under veil
Of her own golden hair. The woods among,
They wander'd up and down with fond delay,
Nor marked the fall of ev'ning ; parted then,
The happiest pair on whom the sun declin'd.
Next day he found her on a flowery bank,
Half under shade of willows, by a spring,
The mirror of the swains, that o'er the meads,
Slow-winding, scatter'd flowerets in its way.

    [1] Burns noticed these lines and adopts them in his song, " O wert
thou in the cauld blast."

Thro' many a winding walk and alley green,
She led him to her garden. Wonder-struck,
He gazed, all eye, o'er th'enchanting scene :
And much he praised the walks, the groves, the flowers
Her beautiful creation ; much he praised
The beautiful creatress ; and awaked
The echo in her praise. Like the first pair,
Adam and Eve in Eden's blissful bowers,
When newly come from their Creator's hand,
Our lovers lived in joy. Here, day by day,
In fond endearments, in embraces sweet,
That lovers only know, they lived, they loved,
And found the paradise that Adam lost.
Nor did the virgin, with false modest pride,
Retard the nuptial morn : she fixed the day
That blessed the youth, and opened to his eyes
An age of gold, the heav'n of happiness
That lovers in their lucid moments dream.
  And now the Morning, like a rosy bride
Adorned on her day, put on her robes,
Her beauteous robes of light : the Naiad streams,
Sweet as the cadence of a poet's song,
Flowed down the dale : the voices of the grove
And every winged warbler of the air,
Sung overhead, and there was joy in heav'n.
Ris'n with the dawn, the bride and bridal-maids
Strayed thro' the woods, and o'er the vales, in quest
Of flowers and garlands, and sweet-smelling herbs,
To strew the bridegroom's way, and deck his bed.
  Fair in the bosom of the level Loch
Rose a green island, cover'd with a spring
Of flowers perpetual, goodly to the eye,
And blooming from afar. High in the midst,
Between two fountains, an enchanted tree
Grew ever green and every month renewed

Its blooms and apples of Hesperian gold,
Here ev'ry bride (as ancient poets sing)
Two golden apples gathered from the bough,
To give the bridegroom in the bed of love,
The pledge of nuptial concord and delight
For many a coming year. Levina now
Had reach'd the isle, with an attendant maid,
And pulled the mystic apples, pulled the fruit ;
But wished and longed for the enchanted tree.
Not fonder sought the first created fair
The fruit forbidden of the mortal tree,
The source of human woe. Two plants arose
Fair by the mother's side, with fruits and flowers
In miniature. One, with audacious hand,
In evil hour she rooted from the ground.
At once the island shook, and shrieks of woe
At times were heard, amid the troubled air.
Her whole frame shook, the blood forsook her face,
Her knees knocked, and her heart within her died.
Trembling and pale, and boding woes to come,.
They seized the boat, and hurried from the isle.
And now they gain'd the middle of the loch,
And saw th'approaching land : now, wild with joy,
They row'd, they flew. When lo ! at once effused,
Sent by the angry demon of the isle,
A whirlwind rose : it lashed the furious Lake
To tempest, overturned the boat, and sunk
The fair Levina to a watery tomb.
Her sad companions, bending from a rock,
Thrice saw her head, and supplicating hands
Held up to Heaven, and heard the shriek of death :
Then overhead the parting billow closed,
And op'd no more. Her fate in mournful lays,
The Muse relates ; and sure each tender maid
For her shall heave the sympathetic sigh,

And happ'ly my Eumelia,[1] (for her soul
Is pity's self,) as, void of household cares,
Her evening walk she bends beside the Loch,
Which yet retains her name, shall sadly drop
A tear, in mem'ry of the hapless maid,
And mourn with me the sorrows of the youth
Whom from his mistress death did not divide.
Robbed of the calm possession of his mind,
All night he wandered by the sounding shore,
Long looking o'er the loch, and saw at times
The dear, the dreary ghost of her he loved ;
Till love and grief subdued his manly prime,
And brought his youth with sorrow to the grave.
I know an aged swain, whose hoary head[2]
Was bent with years, the village chronicler,
Who much had seen, and from the former times
Much had received. He, hanging o'er the hearth
In winter evenings, to the gaping swains,
And children circling round the fire, would tell
Stories of old, and tales of other times.
Of Lomond and Levina he would talk ;
And how of old, in Britain's evil days,
When brothers against brothers drew the sword
Of civil rage, the hostile hand of war
Ravaged the land, gave cities to the sword,
And all the country to devouring fire.
Then these fair forests and Elysian scenes,
In one great conflagration, flamed to heaven.
Barren and black, by swift degrees arose
A muirish fen ; and hence the labouring hind,
Digging for fuel, meets the mouldering trunks
Of oaks, and branchy antlers of the deer.

[1] Margaret White, also described as Peggie, noticed elsewhere.

[2] A description of the poet's father, his fireside and locality.

Now sober Industry, illustrious Power !
Hath raised the peaceful cottage, calm abode
Of Innocence and Joy : now, sweating, guides
The shining ploughshare ; tames the stubborn soil ;
Leads the long drain along th'unfertile marsh ;
Bids the bleak hill with vernal verdure bloom,
The haunt of flocks : and clothes the barren heath
With waving harvests, and the golden grain.
    Fair from his hand, behold the Village rise[1]
In rural pride, 'mong intermingled trees !
Above whose aged tops the joyful swains
At even-tide, descending from the hill,
With eye enamoured, mark the many wreaths
Of pillared smoke, high-curling to the clouds.
The street resounds with Labour's various voice,[2]
Who whistles at his work. Gay on the green,
Young blooming boys, and girls with golden hair,
Trip nimble-footed, wanton in their play,
The village hope. All in a reverend row,
Their grey-haired grandsires, sitting in the sun,[3]
Before the gate, and leaning on the staff,
The well-remembered stories of their youth
Recount, and shake their aged locks with joy.
    How fair a prospect rises to the eye,[4]
Where beauty vies in all her vernal forms,
For ever pleasant, and for ever new !
Swells th' exulting thought, expands the soul,
Drowning each ruder care : a blooming train
Of bright ideas rushes on the mind.
Imagination rouses at the scene,
And backward, thro' the gloom of ages past,

[1] A description of his native place, Kinnesswood.
[2] The weavers at their loom.
[3] The village green, now disappeared.
[4] The view from the Poet's Walk, looking south.

Beholds Arcadia, like a rural Queen,
Encircled with her swains and rosy nymphs,
The mazy dance conducting on the green.
Nor yield to old Arcadia's blissful vales
Thine, gentle Leven ! green on either hand
Thy meadows spread, unbroken of the plough,
With beauty all their own.   Thy fields rejoice
With all the riches of the golden year.
Fat on the plain and mountain's sunny side,
Large droves of oxen, and the fleecy flocks
Feed undisturb'd and fill the echoing air
With music, grateful to the master's ear.
The traveller stops, and gazes round and round
O'er all the scenes, that animate his heart
With mirth and music.   Even the mendicant,
Bowbent with age, that on the old grey stone,
Sole sitting, suns him in the public way,
Feels his heart leap, and to himself he sings.
    How beautiful around the Loch outspreads
Its wealth of waters, the surrounding vales
Renews, and holds a mirror to the sky,
Perpetual fed by many sister-streams,
Haunts of the angler ! First the gulfy Po,
That through the quaking marsh and waving reeds
Creeps slow and silent on.   The rapid Queech,
Whose foaming torrents o'er the broken steep
Burst down impetuous, with the placid wave
Of flowery Leven, for the canine pike
And silver eel renown'd.   But chief thy stream
O Gairney ! sweetly winding, claims the song.
First on thy banks the Doric reed I tun'd,
Stretch'd on the verdant grass ; while twilight meek,
Enrob'd in mist, slow sailing thro' the air,
Silent and still, on every closed flower
Shed drops nectarious ; and around the fields

No noise was heard, save where the whisp'ring reeds
Wav'd to the breeze, or in the dusky air
The slow-wing'd crane mov'd heav'ly o'er the lee,
And shrilly clamour'd as he sought his rest,
There would I sit, and tune some youthful lay,
Or watch the motion of the living fires,
That day and night their never-ceasing course
Wheel round th'eternal poles, and bend the knee
To Him the Maker of yon starry sky,
Omnipotent ! who, thron'd above all heav'ns,
Yet ever present through the peopl'd space
Of vast Creation's infinite extent,
Pours life, and bliss, and beauty, pours Himself,
His own essential goodness, o'er the minds
Of happy beings, through ten thousand worlds.
   Nor shall the Muse forget thy friendly heart,
O Laelius ! partner of my youthful hours[1] ;
How often, rising from the bed of peace,
We would walk forth to meet the summer morn,
Inhaling health and harmony of mind ;
Philosophers and friends ; while science beam'd
With ray divine as lovely on our minds
As yonder orient sun, whose welcome light
Reveal'd the vernal landscape to the view.
Yet oft, unbending from more serious thought,
Much of the looser follies of mankind,
Hum'rous and gay, we'd talk, and much would laugh ;
While, ever and anon, their foibles vain
Imagination off'rd to our view.
   Fronting where Gairney pours his silent urn
Into the Loch, an island lifts its head.[2]

[1] The poet's student friend, George Henderson, son of the laird of Turfhills, with whom he resided on several occasions.

[2] St. Serf's Isle, the home of the Culdee missionaries, their buildings and graveyard.

THE CHAPEL ON ST. SERF'S ISLAND, LOCHLEVEN

As it appeared in 1850

Grassy and wild, with ancient ruin heap'd
Of cells ; where from the noisy world retir'd
Of old, as same reports, Religion dwelt
Safe from the insults of the darken'd crowd
That bow'd the knee to Odin ; and in times
Of ignorance, when Caledonia's sons
(Before the triple-crowned giant fell)
Exchang'd their simple faith for Rome's deceits.
Here Superstition for her cloister'd sons
A dwelling rear'd, with many an arched vault ;
Where her pale vot'ries at the midnight hour,
In many a mournful strain of melancholy,
Chanted their orisons to the cold moon.
It now resounds with the wild-shrieking gull
The crested lapwing, and the clamorous mew.
The patient heron, and the bittern dull,
Deep-sounding in the base, with all the tribe
That by the water seek th'appointed meal.
    From thence the shepherd in the fenced fold,
'Tis said, has heard strange sounds, and music wild ;
Such as in Selma, by the burning oak
Of hero fallen, or of battle lost,
Warn'd Fingal's mighty son, from trembling chords
Of untouch'd harp, self-sounding in the night.
Perhaps th'afflicted Genius of the Loch,
That leaves the wat'ry grot, each night to mourn
The waste of time, his desolated isles
And temples in the dust : his plaintive voice
Is heard resounding through the dreary courts
Of high Lochleven Castle, famous once,
Th' abode of heroes of the Bruce's line ;
Gothic the pile, and high the solid walls,
With warlike ramparts, and the strong defence
Of jutting battlements, an age's toil !
No more its arches echo to the noise

Of joy and festive mirth. No more the glance
Of blazing taper through its windows beams,
And quivers on the undulating wave :
But naked stand the melancholy walls,
Lash'd by the wintry tempests, cold and bleak,
That whistle mournful thro' the empty halls,
And piece-meal crumble down the tow'rs to dust.
Perhaps in some lone, dreary, desert tower,
That time has spar'd, forth from the window looks,
Half hid in grass the solitary fox,[1]
While from above, the owl, musician dire !
Screams hideous, harsh, and grating to the ear.
   Equal in age, and sharers of its fate,
A row of moss-grown trees around it stand.
Scarce here and there, upon their blasted tops,
A shrivell'd leaf distinguishes the year ;
Emblem of hoary age, the eve of life,
When man draws nigh his everlasting home,
Within a step of the devouring grave,
When all his views and tow'ring hopes are gone,
And ev'ry appetite before him dead.
Bright shines the morn, while in the ruddy east
The sun hangs hovering o'er the Atlantic wave.
Apart, on yonder green hill's sunny side,
Seren'd with all the music of the morn,
Attentive let me sit ; while from the rock,
The swains, laborious, roll the limestone huge.
Bounding elastic from th' indented grass,
At every fall it springs, and thund'ring shoots,
O'er rocks and precipices, to the plain.
And let the shepherd careful tend his flock
Far from the dang'rous steep ; nor, O ye swains !
Stray heedless of its rage.   Behold the tears

[1] A stem of the digitalis plant.

K

Yon wretched widow o'er the mangled corpse[1]
Of her dead husband pours, who, hapless man !
Cheerful and strong went forth at rising morn
To usual toil ; but, ere the evening hour,
His sad companion bore him lifeless home.
Urg'd from the hill's high top, with progress swift,
A weighty stone, resistless, rapid came,
Seen by the fated wretch, who stood unmov'd,
Nor turn'd to fly, till flight had been in vain ;
When now arriv'd the instrument of death,
And fell'd him to the ground. The thirsty land
Drank up his blood : such was the will of Heav'n.

How wide the landscape opens to the view
Still as I mount, the less'ning hills decline,
Till high above them northern Grampius lifts
His hoary head, bending beneath a load
Of everlasting snow. O'er southern fields
I see the Cheviot hills, the ancient bounds[2]
Of two contending kingdoms. There in fight
Brave Percy and the gallant Douglas bled,
The house of heroes, and the death of hosts !
Wat'ring the fertile fields, majestic Forth,
Full, deep, and wide, rolls placid to the sea,
With many a vessel trim and oarèd bark
In rich profusion cover'd, wafting o'er
The wealth and product of far distant lands.

But chief mine eye on the subjected vale
Of Leven pleas'd looks down ; while o'er the trees,
That shield the hamlet with the shade of years,
The towering smoke of early fire ascends,
And the shrill cock proclaims the advanced morn.

---

[1] This refers to the rolling of lime-rock down the hill to be burnt in kilns below, by which a workman was killed.

[2] As seen from the Lomond Hill on a clear day.

How blest the man who in these peaceful plains,[1]
Ploughs his paternal field ; far from the noise,
The care, and bustle of a busy world.
All in the sacred, sweet, sequester'd vale
Of Solitude, the secret flowery-path
Of rural life, he dwells ; and with him dwells
Peace and Content, twins of the sylvan shade,
And all the Graces of the golden age.
Such is Agricola, the wise, the good,
By nature formed for the calm retreat,
The silent path of life.   Learn'd, but not fraught
With self-importance, as the starchèd fool ;
Who challenges respect by solemn face,
By studied accent, and high-sounding phrase.
Enamour'd of the shade, but not morose.
Politeness, rais'd in courts by frigid rules,
With him spontaneous grows.   Not books alone,
But man his study, and the better part ;
To tread the ways of virtue, and to act
The various scenes of life with God's applause.
Deep in the bottom of this flow'ry vale,
With blooming sallows, and the leafy twine
Of verdant alders fenc'd, his dwelling stands[2]
Complete in rural elegance.   The door,
By which the poor or pilgrim never pass'd,
Still open, speaks the master's bounteous heart.
There, O how sweet ! amid the fragrant shrubs
At ev'ning cool to sit ; while on their boughs,
The nested songsters twitter o'er their young,
And the hoarse low of folded cattle breaks
The silence, wafted o'er the sleeping Loch,

[1] Mr. Arnot of Portmoak.

[2] Hedges of verdant alders were formerly common in the gardens of Kinnesswood.

Whose waters glow beneath the purple tinge
Of western cloud ; while converse sweet deceives
The stealing foot of time. Or where the ground,
Mounded irregular, points out the graves
Of our forefathers, and the hallow'd fane,
Where swains assembling worship, let us walk,
In softly-soothing melancholy thought,
As night's seraphic bard, immortal Young,
Or sweet-complaining Gray ; there see the goal
Of human life, where drooping, faint, and tir'd
Oft missed the prize,—the weary racer rests.
    Thus sung the youth, amid unfertile wilds[1]
And nameless deserts, unpoetic ground !
Far from his friends he stray'd, recording thus
The dear remembrance of his native fields,
To cheer the tedious night ; while slow disease
Prey'd on his pining vitals, and the blasts
Of dark December shook his humble cot.

[1] Written while Bruce was located at Forest Mill, and his surroundings there are noted.

KINNESSWOOD

As seen from the hill, with part of Lochleven, St. Serf's Isle, Benarty Hill, Blairadam and Cleish Hill on the right.

VERNAL ODE

See ! see ! the genial Spring again
Unbind the glebe and paint the plain.
The garden blooms : the tulips gay
For thee put on their best array ;
And ev'ry flower so richly dight
In spangled robes of varying light.
From noisy towns and noxious sky,
Hither Amelia ! haste and fly.
View these gay scenes ; their sweets inhale :
Health breathes in ev'ry balmy gale :
Nor fear lest the returning storm
The vernal season may deform.
For hark ! I hear the swallows sing,
Who ne'er uncertain tidings bring :

They with glad voice proclaim on high,
" The Spring is come, the Summer's nigh ! "
Sweet bird ! what sacred lore is thine,
The change of seasons to divine ?
Thou countest no revolving day
By solar or sidereal ray :
No clock hast thou, with busy chime
To tell the silent lapse of time—
To call thee from thy drowsy cell.
'Tis Heav'n that rings thy matin bell.
Strait all the chatt'ring tribe obey ;
Start from their trance, and wing away :
To their lov'd summer seats repair ;
And ev'ry pinion floats on air.

Miscellaneous Pieces

WEAVING SPIRITUALISED

This was written to his brother James, when he heard that he had begun to learn weaving.

A WEB I hear thou hast begun,
And know'st not when it may be done—
So death uncertain see ye fear—
For ever distant, ever near.

See'st thou the shuttle quickly pass—
Think mortal life is as the grass,—
An empty cloud,—a morning dream—
A bubble rising on the stream.

The knife still ready to cut off
Excrescent knots that mar the stuff,
To stern affliction's rod compare—
'Tis for thy good, so learn to bear.

Too full a quill oft checks the speed
Of shuttle flying by the reed—
So riches oft keep back the soul,
That else would hasten to its goal.

Thine eye the web runs keenly o'er
For things amiss, unseen before—
Thus scan thy life—mend what's amiss—
Next day correct the faults of this.

For when the web is at an end,
'Tis then too late a fault to mend—
Let thought of this awaken dread—
Repentance dwells not with the dead.

THE LAST DAY

This poem was written while Michael Bruce attended the Edinburgh University, but was omitted by Logan, when editing Bruce's poems, which he issued in 1770, though he afterwards used portions of it in the piece he published, named " Runnamede." We are indebted to Mr. John Birrell for discovering a MS.copy of it in Bruce's writing in his mother's cottage.

His second coming, who at first appeared
To save the world, but now to judge mankind
According to their works ;—the trumpet's sound,—
The dead arising, the wide world in flames,—
The mansions of the blest, and the dire pit
Of Satan and of woe,—O Muse ! unfold.
    O Thou ! Whose eye the future and the past
In one broad view beholdest—from the first
Of days, when o'er this rude unformèd mass
Light, first-born of existence, smiling rose,
Down to that latest moment, when thy voice
Shall bid the sun be darkness, when thy hand
Shall blot creation out,—assist my song !
Thou only know'st, who gav'st these orbs to roll
Their destin'd circles, when their course shall set ;
When ruin and destruction fierce shall ride
In triumph o'er creation. This is hid,
In kindness unto man. Thou giv'st to know
The event certain : angels know not when.[1]
    'Twas on an autumn's eve, serene and calm.
I walked attendant on the funeral
Of an old swain : around, the village crowd
Loquacious chatted, till we reached the place

[1] Matt. xxiv. 36.

136

Where, shrouded up, the sons of other years
Lie silent in the grave. The sexton there
Had digg'd the bed of death, the narrow house
For all that live, appointed. To the dust
We gave the dead. Then moralizing home
The swains return'd, to drown in copious bowls
The labours of the day, and thoughts of death.

    The sun now trembled at the western gate ;
His yellow ray stream'd in the fleecy clouds.
I sat me down upon a broad flat stone ;
And much I mused on the changeful state
Of sublunary things. The joys of life,
How frail, how short, how passing ! As the sea,
Now flowing, thunders on the rocky shore ;
Now lowly ebbing leaves a tract of sand,
Waste, wide and dreary : so, in this vain world,
Through every varying state of life, we toss
In endless fluctuation ; till, tir'd out
With sad variety of bad and worse,
We reach life's period, reach the blissful port,
Where change affects not, and the weary rest.

    Then sure the sun which lights us to our shroud,
Than that which gave us first to see the light,
Is happier far. As he who, hopeless, long
Hath rode th' Atlantic billow, from the mast,
Skirting the blue horizon, sees the land,
His native land approach ; joy fills his heart,
And swells each throbbing vein : so, here confin'd
We weary tread life's long, long toilsome maze ;
Still hoping, vainly hoping, for relief,
And rest from labour. Ah ! mistaken thought :
To seek in life what only death can give.
But what is death ? Is it an endless sleep,
Unconscious of the present and the past,
And never to be waken'd ? Sleeps the soul ;

Nor wakes ev'n in a dream ?   If it is so,
Happy the sons of pleasure ;   they have liv'd
And made the most of life :   and foolish he,
The sage, who, dreaming of hereafter, grudg'd
Himself the tasting of the sweets of life,
And call'd it temperance ;   and hop'd for joys
More durable and sweet, beyond the grave.
Vain is the poet's song, the soldier's toil !
Vain is the sculptur'd marble and the bust !
How vain to hope for never-dying fame,
If souls can die !   But that they never die,
This thirst of glory whispers.   Wherefore gave
The great Creator such a strong desire
He never meant to satisfy ?   These stones,
Memorials of the dead, with rustic art
And rude inscription cut, declare the soul
Immortal.   Man, form'd for eternity,
Abhors annihilation, and the thought
Of dark oblivion.   Hence, with ardent wish
And vigorous effort, each would fondly raise
Some lasting monument, to save his name
Safe from the waste of years.   Hence Caesar fought ;
Hence Raphael painted ; and hence Milton sung.
    Thus musing, sleep oppress'd my drowsy sense,
And wrapt me into rest.   Before mine eyes,
Fair as the morn, when up the flaming east
The sun ascends, a radiant seraph stood,
Crown'd with a wreath of palm :   his golden hair
Wav'd on his shoulders, girt with shining plumes ;
From which, down to the ground, loose-floating trail'd,
In graceful negligence, his heavenly robe :
Upon his face, flush'd with immortal youth,
Unfading beauty bloom'd ;   and thus he spake :
    " Well hast thou judged ; the soul must be immortal !
And that it is, this awful day declares ;

This day, the last that e'er the sun shall gild :
Arrested by Omnipotence, no more
Shall he describe the year : the moon no more
Shall shed her borrow'd light. This is the day
Seal'd in the rolls of Fate, when o'er the dead
Almighty power shall wake and raise to life
The sleeping myriads. Now shall be approv'd
The ways of God to man, and all the clouds
Of Providence be clear'd : now shall be disclos'd
Why vice in purple oft upon a throne
Exalted sat, and shook her iron scourge
O'er virtue, lowly seated on the ground :
Now deeds committed in the sable shade
Of eyeless darkness, shall be brought to light ;
And every act shall meet its just reward."
    As thus he spake, the morn arose ; and sure
Methought ne'er rose a fairer. Not a cloud
Spotted the blue expanse ; and not a gale
Breath'd o'er the surface of the dewy earth.
Twinkling with yellow lustre, the gay birds
On every blooming spray sung their sweet lays,
And prais'd their great Creator ; through the fields
The lowing cattle graz'd ; and all around
Was beauty, happiness, and mirth, and love.—
" All these thou seest "(resumed the angelic power)
" No more shall give thee pleasure. Thou must leave
This world ; of which now come and see the end."
    This said, he touch'd me, and such strength infus'd
That as he soared up the pathless air,
I lightly followed. On the awful peak
Of an eternal rock, against whose base
The sounding billows beat, he set me down.
I heard a noise, loud as a rushing stream,
When o'er the rugged precipice it roars,
And foaming, thunders on the rocks below.

Astonished, I gaz'd around ; when lo !
I saw an angel down from Heaven descend.
His face was as the sun ; his dreadful height
Such as the statue, by the Grecian plan'd,
Of Philip's son, Athos, with all his rocks,
Moulded into a man : One foot on earth,
And one upon the rolling sea, he fix'd.
As when, at setting sun, the rainbow shines
Refulgent, meting out the half of Heav'n—
So stood he ; and, in act to speak he rais'd
His shining hand.   His voice was as the sound
Of many waters, or the deep-mouthed roar
Of thunder, when it bursts the riven cloud,
And bellows through the ether. Nature stood
Silent in all her works : while thus he spake :
" Hear, thou that roll'st above, thou radiant sun !
Ye heavens and earth attend ! while I declare
The will of the Eternal.   By his name
Who lives, and shall for ever live, I swear
That time shall be no longer."[1]
     He disappear'd.   Fix'd in deep thought I stood
At what would follow.   Straight another sound ;
To which the Nile, o'er Ethiopia's rocks
Rushing in one broad cataract, were naught.
It seem'd as if the pillars that upheld
The universe had fall'n ; and all its worlds,
Unhing'd, had strove together for the way,
In cumbrous crashing ruin.   Such the roar !
A sound that might be felt ; it pierc'd beyond
The limits of creation.   Chaos roar'd ;
And heav'n and earth return'd the mighty noise.—
" Thou hear'st," said then my heav'nly guide, " the sound
Of the last trumpet.   See, where from the clouds
Th'archangel Michael, one of the seven ·

[1] Rev. x. 5. 6.

140

That minister before the throne of God,
Leans forward ; and the sonorous tube inspires
With breath immortal. By his side the sword
Which, like a meteor, o'er the vanquish'd head
Of Satan hung, when he rebellious rais'd
War, and embroil'd the happy fields above."
    A pause ensued. The fainting sun grew pale,
And seem'd to struggle through a sky of blood ;
While dim eclipse impair'd his beam : the earth
Shook to her deepest centre ; Ocean rag'd,
And dash'd his billows on the frighted shore.
All was confusion. Heartless, helpless, wild,
As flocks of timid sheep, or driven deer,
Wand'ring, th' inhabitants of earth appear'd :
Terror in every look, and pale affright
Sat in each eye ; amazed at the past,
And for the future trembling. All call'd great,
Or deem'd illustrious, by erring man,
Was now no more. The hero and the prince,
Their grandeur lost, now mingled with the crowd ;
And all distinctions, those except from faith
And virtue flowing : these upheld the soul,
As ribb'd with triple steel. All else were lost !
    Now, vain is greatness ! as the morning clouds,
That, rising, promise rain : condens'd they stand,
Till, touch'd by winds, they vanish into air.
The farmer mourns : so mourns the helpless wretch,
Who, cast by fortune from some envied height,
Finds nought within him to support his fall.
High as his hopes had rais'd him, low he sinks
Below his fate, in comfortless despair.—
Who would not laugh at an attempt to build
A lasting structure on the rapid stream
Of foaming Tigris, the foundations laid
Upon the glassy surface ? Such the hopes

Of him whose views are bounded to this world :
Immers'd in his own labour'd work, he dreams
Himself secure ; when, on a sudden down,
Torn from its sandy ground, the fabric falls !
He starts, and, waking, finds himself undone.[1]
    Not so the man who on religion's base
His hope and virtue founds.   Firm on the Rock
Of ages his foundation laid, remains,
Above the frowns of fortune or her smiles ;
In every varying state of life, the same.
Nought fears he from the world, and nothing hopes.
With unassuming courage, inward strength
Endu'd, resign'd to Heaven, he leads a life
Superior to the common herd of men,
Whose joys, connected with the changeful flood
Of fickle fortune, ebb and flow with it.
    Nor is religion a chimera : Sure
'Tis something real.   Virtue cannot live,
Divided from it.   As a sever'd branch
It withers, pines, and dies.   Who loves not God,
That made him, and preserv'd, nay more—redeem'd,
Is dangerous.   Can ever gratitude
Bind him who spurns at these most sacred ties ?
Say, can he, in the silent scenes of life,
Be sociable ?   Can he be a friend ?
At best, he must but feign.   The worst of brutes
An atheist is ;   for beasts acknowledge God.
The lion, with the terrors of his mouth,
Pays homage to his Maker ;   the grim wolf,
At midnight, howling, seeks his meat from God.
    Again th' archangel raised his dreadful voice ;
Earth trembled at the sound.   " Awake, ye dead !
And come to judgment."   At the mighty call,
As armies issue at the trumpet's sound,

[1] Matt. viii. 24.

So rose the dead. A shaking first I heard.[1]
And bone together came unto his bone,
Though sever'd by wide seas and distant lands.
A spirit liv'd within them. He who made,
Wound up, and set in motion, the machine,
To run unhurt the length of fourscore years,
Who knows the structure of each secret spring ;
Can He not join again the sever'd parts,
And join them with advantage ? This to man
Hard and impossible may seem ; to God
Is easy. Now, through all the darken'd air,
The living atoms flew, each to his place,
And nought was missing in the great account,
Down from the dust of him whom Cain first slew,
To him who yesterday was laid in earth,
And scarce had seen corruption ; whether in
The bladed grass they cloth'd the verdant plain,
Or smil'd in opening flowers ; or, in the sea,
Became the food of monsters of the Deep,
Or pass'd in transmigrations infinite
Through ev'ry kind of being. None mistakes
His kindred matter ; but, by sympathy
Combining, rather by Almighty Pow'r
Led on, they closely mingle and unite
But chang'd : for, subject to decay no more,
Or dissolution, deathless as the soul,
The body is ; and fitted to enjoy
Eternal bliss, or bear eternal pain.
    As when in Spring the sun's prolific beams
Have wak'd to life the insect tribes, that sport
And wanton in his rays at ev'ning mild,
Proud of their new existence, up the air,
In devious circles wheeling, they ascend,
Innumerable ; the whole air is dark :

[1] Ezek. xxxvii. 7.

So, by the trumpet rous'd, the sons of men,
In countless numbers, cover'd all the ground,
From frozen Greenland to the southern pole ;
All who e'er liv'd on earth. See Lapland's sons,
Whose zenith is the pole ; a barb'rous race !
Rough as their storms, and savage as their clime,
Unpolished as their bears, and but in shape
Distinguish'd from them : Reason's dying lamp
Scarce brighter burns than instinct in their breast.
With wand'ring Russians, and all those who dwelt
In Scandinavia, by the Baltic Sea ;
The rugged Pole, with Prussia's warlike race :
Germania pours her numbers, where the Rhine
And mighty Danube pour their flowing urns.

Behold thy children, Britain ! hail the light :
A manly race, whose business was arms,
And long uncivilised ; yet, train'd to deeds
Of virtue, they withstood the Roman power,
And made their eagles droop. On Morven's coast,
A race of heroes and of bards arise ;
The mighty Fingal, and his mighty son,
Who launch'd the spear, and touch'd the tuneful harp :
With Scotia's chiefs, the sons of later years,
Her Kenneths and her Malcolms, warriors fam'd ;
Her generous Wallace, and her gallant Bruce.
See, in her pathless wilds, where the grey stones
Are raised in memory of the mighty dead.
Armies arise of English, Scots, and Picts ;
And giant Danes, who from bleak Norway's coast,
Ambitious, came to conquer her fair fields,[1]
And chain her sons : But Scotia gave them graves !
Behold the kings that fill'd the English throne !
Edwards and Henrys, names of deathless fame,
Start from the tomb. Immortal William ! see,
Surrounding angels point him from the rest,

[1] The battle of Largs.

Who saved the State from tyranny and Rome.
Behold her poets ! Shakespeare, fancy's child ;
Spenser, who, through his smooth and moral tale,
Yet points fair virtue out ; with him who sung
Of man's first disobedience.[1] Young lifts up
His awful head, and joys to see the day,
The great, th' important day, of which he sung.
  See where imperial Rome exalts her height !
Her senators and gowned fathers rise ;
Her consuls, who, as ants without a king,
Went forth to conquer kings ; and at their wheels
In triumph led the chiefs of distant lands.
Behold, in Cannæ's field, what hostile swarms
Burst from th'ensanguin'd ground, where Hannibal
Shook Rome through all her legions : Italy
Trembled unto the Capitol. If fate
Had not withstood th' attempt, she now had bow'd
Her head to Carthage. See, Pharsalia pours
Her murder'd thousands ! who, in the last strife
Of Rome for dying liberty, were slain,
To make a man the master of the world.
  All Europe's sons throng forward ; numbers vast !
Imagination fails beneath the weight.
What numbers yet remain ! Th'enervate race
Of Asia, from where Tanais rolls
O'er rocks and dreary wastes his foaming stream,
To where the Eastern Ocean thunders round
The spicy Java ; with the tawny race
That dwelt in Afric, from the Red Sea, north,
To the Cape, south, where the rude Hottentot
Sinks into brute ; with those, who long unknown
Till by Columbus found, a naked race,
And only skill'd to urge the sylvan war ;
That peopled the wide continent that spreads

---

[1] As in Milton.

L

From rocky Zembla, whiten'd with the snow
Of twice three thousand years, south to the Straits
Nam'd from Magellan, where the ocean roars
Round earth's remotest bounds. Now, had not He
The great Creator of the universe,
Enlarg'd the wide foundations of the world,
Room had been wanting to the mighty crowds
That pour'd from every quarter. At his word,
Obedient angels stretch'd an ample plain,
Where dwelt His people in the Holy Land,
Fit to contain the whole of human race—
As when the autumn, yellow on the fields,
Invites the sickle, forth the farmer sends
His servants to cut down and gather in
The bearded grain : so, by Jehovah sent,
His angels, from all corners of the world,
Led on the living and awaken'd dead
To judgment ; as, in th'Apocalypse,
John, gather'd, saw the people of the earth,
And kings, to Armageddon—Now look round
Thou whose ambitious heart for glory beats !
See all the wretched things on earth call'd great,
And lifted up to gods ! How little now
Seems all their grandeur ! See the conqueror,
Mad Alexander, who his victor arms
Bore o'er the then known globe, then sat him down
And wept, because he had no other world
To give to desolation ; how he droops !
He knew not, hapless wretch ! he never learn'd
The harder conquest—to subdue himself.
Now is the Christian's triumph, now he lifts
His head on high ; while down the dying hearts
Of sinners helpless sink : black guilt distracts
And wrings their tortur'd souls ; while every thought
Is big with keen remorse, or dark despair.

But now a nobler subject claims the song.
My mind recoils at the amazing theme ;
For how shall finite think of infinite ?
How shall a stripling, by the muse untaught,
Sing Heaven's Almighty, prostrate at whose feet
Archangels fall ?   Unequal to the task,
I dare the bold attempt : assist me, Heaven !
From Thee begun, with Thee shall end my song !
   Now, down from th' opening firmament,
Seated upon a sapphire throne, high rais'd
Upon an azure ground, upheld by wheels
Of emblematic structure, as a wheel
Had been within a wheel, studded with eyes
Of flaming fire, and by four cherubs led ;
I saw the Judge descend. Around Him came,
By thousands and by millions, heaven's bright host.
About Him blaz'd insufferable light,
Invisible as darkness to the eye.
His car above the mount of Olives stay'd
Where last with His disciples He convers'd,
And left them gazing as He soar'd aloft.
He darkness as a curtain drew around ;
On which the colour of the rainbow shone,
Various and bright ; and from within was heard
A voice, as deep-mouth'd thunder, speaking thus :
" Go, Raphael, and from these reprobate
Divide my chosen saints ; go separate
My people from among them, as the wheat
Is in the harvest sever'd from the tares :
Set them upon the right, and on the left
Leave these ungodly. Thou, Michael, choose,
From forth th' angelic host, a chosen band,
And Satan with his legions hither bring
To judgment, from hell's caverns ; whither fled,
They think to hide from my awaken'd wrath,

Which chas'd them out of Heaven, and which they dread
More than the horrors of the pit, which now
Shall be redoubled sevenfold on their heads."
    Swift as conception, at his bidding flew
His ministers, obedient to his word.
And, as a shepherd, who all day hath fed
His sheep and goats promiscuous, but at eve
Dividing, shuts them up in different folds :
So now the good were parted from the bad ;
For ever parted ; never more to join
And mingle as on earth, where often pass'd
For each other ; ev'n close Hypocrisy
Escapes not, but, unask'd, alike the scorn
Of vice and virtue stands. Now separate,
Upon the right appear'd a dauntless, firm,
Composèd number : joyful at the thought
Of immortality, they forward look'd
With hope unto the future ; conscience, pleas'd,
Smiling, reflects upon a well-spent life ;
Heaven dawns within their breasts. The other crew,
Pale and dejected, scarcely lift their heads
To view the hated light : his trembling hand
Each lays upon his guilty face ; and now,
In gnawings of the never-dying worm,
Begins a hell that never shall be quench'd.
    But now the enemy of God and man,
Cursing his fate, comes forward, led in chains,
Infrangible, of burning adamant,
Hewn from the rocks of Hell ; now too the bands
Of rebel angels, who long time had walk'd
The world, and by their oracles deceiv'd
The blinded nations, or by secret guile
Wrought men to vice, came on, raging in vain,
And struggling with their fetters, which, as fate,
Compell'd them fast. They wait their dreadful doom.

Now from His lofty throne, with eyes that blaz'd
Intolerable day, th' Almighty Judge
Look'd down awhile upon the subject crowd.
As when a caravan of merchants, led
By thirst of gain to travel the parch'd sands
Of waste Arabia, hears a lion roar,
The wicked trembled at His view ; upon
The ground they roll'd, in pangs of wild despair
To hide their faces, which not blushes mark'd
But livid horror. Conscience, who asleep
Long time had lain, now lifts her snaky head,
And frights them into madness ; while the list
Of all their sins she offers to their view :
For she had power to hurt them, and her sting
Was as a scorpion's. He who never knew
Its wound is happy, though a fetter'd slave,
Chain'd to the oar, or to the dark damp mine
Confin'd ; while he who sits upon a throne,
Under her frown, is wretched. But the damn'd
Alone can tell what 'tis to feel her scourge
In all its horrors, with her poison'd sting
Fix'd in their hearts. This is the second Death.
Upon the Book of Life He laid His hand,
Clos'd with the seal of Heaven ; which op'd, He read
The names of the Elect. God knows His own.[1]
" Come " (looking on the right, He mildly said),
" Ye of My Father blessed ere the world
Was moulded out of chaos—ere the sons
Of God exulting, sung at Nature's birth :
For you I left my throne, my glory left,
And, shrouded up in clay, I weary walk'd
Your world, and many miseries endur'd :
Death was the last. For you I died, that you
Might live with me for ever, and in Heav'n sit

[1] 2 Tim. ii. 19.

149

On thrones, and as the sun in brightness shine
For ever in my kingdom. Faithfully
Have ye approv'd yourselves. I hungry was,
And thirsty, and ye gave me meat and drink ;
Ye clothed me, naked ; when I fainting lay
In all the sad variety of pain,
Ye cheer'd me with the tenderness of friends ;
In sickness and in prison, me reliev'd.
Nay, marvel not that thus I speak : whene'er,
Led by the dictates of fair charity,
Ye help'd the man on whom keen poverty
And wretchedness had laid their meagre hands,
And for my sake, ye did it unto me."[1]
    They heard with joy, and shouting, rais'd their voice
In praise of their Redeemer ! loos'd from earth,
They soar'd triumphant, and at the right hand
Of the great Judge sat down ; who on the left
Now looking stern, with fury in His eyes,
Blasted their spirits, while His arrows, fix'd
Deep in their hearts, in agonizing pain
Scorchèd their vitals, thus their dreadful doom
(More dreadful from those lips which us'd to bless)
He awfully pronounc'd. Earth at His frown
Convulsive trembled ; while the raging deep
Hush'd in a horrid calm his waves. " Depart "
(These, for I heard them, were His awful words !)
" Depart from me, ye cursed ! Oft have I strove
In tenderness and pity to subdue
Your rebel hearts ; as a fond parent bird,
When danger threatens, flutters round her young,
Nature's strong impulse beating in her breast,
Thus ardent did I strive : but all in vain.
Now will I laugh at your calamity,
And mock your fears : as oft, in stupid mirth,

[1] Matt. xxv. 41-45.

Harden'd in wickedness, ye pointed out
The man who labour'd up the steep ascent
Of virtue, to reproach. Depart to fire
Kindled in Tophet for th' arch-enemy,
For Satan and his angels, who, by pride,
Fell into condemnation ; blown up now
To sevenfold fury by th' Almighty breath.
There, in that dreary mansion, where the light
Is solid gloom, darkness that may be felt,[1]
Where hope, the lenient of the ills of life
For ever dies ; there shall ye seek for death,
And shall not find it : for your greatest curse
Is immortality. Omnipotence
Eternally shall punish and preserve."
　　So said He ; and, His hand high lifting, hurl'd
The flashing lightning, and the flaming bolt,
Full on the wicked : kindling in a blaze
The scorchèd earth. Behind, before, around,
The trembling wretches, burst the quiv'ring flames.
They turn'd to fly ; but wrath divine pursu'd
To where, beyond creation's utmost bound,
Where never glimpse of cheerful light arriv'd,
Where scarce e'en thought can travel, but, absorb'd,
Falls headlong down th' immeasurable gulf
Of Chaos—wide and wild, their prison stood—
Of utter darkness, as the horrid shade
That clouds the brow of death. Its open'd mouth
Belch'd sheets of livid flame and pitchy smoke.
Infernal thunders, with explosion dire,
Roar'd through the fiery concave ; while the waves
Of liquid sulphur beat the burning shore
In endless ferment. O'er the dizzy steep
Suspended, wrapt in suffocating gloom,

---

[1] Stretch out thine hand toward heaven, that there may be darkness over the land of Egypt, even darkness which may be felt.—Ex. x. 21.

The sons of black damnation shrieking hung.
Curses unutterable filled their mouths,
Hideous to hear ; their eyes rain'd bitter tears
Of agonizing madness, for their day
Was past, and from their eye repentance hid
For ever ! Round their heads their hissing brands
The Furies wav'd, and o'er the whelming brink
Impetuous urg'd them. In the boiling surge
They headlong fell. The flashing billows roar'd ;
And hell from all her caves return'd the sound.
The gates of flint and tenfold adamant,
With bars of steel, impenetrably firm,
Were shut for ever : the decree of fate,
Immutable, made fast the pond'rous door.
   " Now turn thine eyes," my bright conductor said :
" Behold the world in flames ! so sore the bolts
Of thunder, launch'd by the Almighty arm,
Hath smote upon it. Up the blacken'd air
Ascend the curling flames and billowy smoke ;
And hideous cracklings blot the face of day
With foul eruption. From their inmost beds
The hissing waters rise. Whatever drew
The vital air, or in the spacious deep
Wanton'd at large, expires. Heardst thou that crash ?
There fell the tow'ring Alps, and, dashing down,
Lay bare their centre. See, the flaming mines
Expand their treasures ! no rapacious hand
To seize the precious bane. Now look around :
Say, canst thou tell where stood imperial Rome,
The wonder of the world ; or where the boast
Of Europe, fair Britannia, stretch'd her plain,
Encircled by the ocean ? All is wrapt
In darkness : as (if great may be compar'd
With small) when on Gomorrah's fated field
The flaming sulphur, by Jehovah rain'd,

Sent up a pitchy cloud, killing to life,
And tainting all the air. Another groan !
'Twas Nature's last : and see ! th' extinguish'd sun
Falls devious through the void ; and the fair face
Of Nature is no more ! With sullen joy
Old Chaos views the havoc, and expects
To stretch his sable sceptre o'er the blank
Where once Creation smil'd : o'er which, perhaps,
Creative energy again shall wake,
And into being call a brighter sun,
And fairer worlds ; which, for delightful change,
The saints, descending from the happy seats
Of bliss, shall visit. And, behold ! they rise,
And seek their native land : around them move,
In radiant files, Heaven's host. Immortal wreaths
Of amaranth and roses crown their heads ;
And each a branch of ever-blooming palm
Triumphant holds. In robes of dazzling white
Fairer than that by wintry tempests shed
Upon the frozen ground, array'd they shine,
Fair as the sun when up the steep of Heav'n
He rides in all the majesty of light.
    But who can tell, or if an angel could,
Thou couldst not hear, the glories of the place
For their abode prepar'd ? Though oft on earth
They struggled hard against the stormy tide
Of adverse fortune, and the bitter scorn
Of harden'd villainy—their life a course
Of warfare upon earth ; these toils, when view'd
With the reward, seem nought. The Lord shall guide
Their steps to living fountains, and shall wipe
All tears from ev'ry eye. The wintry clouds
That frown'd on life rack up. A glorious sun
That ne'er shall set, arises in a sky
Unclouded and serene. Their joy is full :

And sickness, pain, and death shall be no more.
   Dost thou desire to follow ? does thy heart
Beat ardent for the prize ? Then tread the path
Religion points to man. What thou hast seen
Fix'd in thy heart retain. For, be assur'd,
In that last moment—in the closing act
Of Nature's drama, ere the hand of fate
Drop the black curtain—thou must bear thy part,
And stand in thine own lot."[1]
                    This said, he stretch'd
His wings, and in a moment left my sight.

HISTORICAL BALLADS

" I never tried anything which fell in with my inclination so. The Historical Ballad is a species of writing by itself. The common people confound it with song, but in truth they are widely different. A song should never be historical. It is generally founded on some thought which must be prosecuted and exhibited in every light with a quickness and turn of expression peculiar to itself. The ballad, again, is founded on some passage of history or (what suits its nature better) of tradition. Here the poet may use his liberty, and cut and carve as he has a mind. I think it a kind of writing remarkably adapted to the Scottish language."—*Extracted from a letter of Michael Bruce to D. Pearson.*

SIR JAMES THE ROSS

AN HISTORICAL BALLAD

OF all the Scottish northern chiefs
   Of high and mighty name,
The bravest was Sir James the Ross,
   A knight of meikle fame.

[1] Dan. xii. 13.

His growth was like a youthful oak
    That crowns the mountain's brow,[1]
And waving o'er his shoulders broad
    His locks of yellow flew.

The chieftain of the brave clan Ross,
    A firm undaunted band ;
Five hundred warriors drew the sword
    Beneath his high command.

In bloody fight thrice had he stood
    Against the English keen—
Ere two-and-twenty op'ning springs
    This noble youth had seen.

The fair Matilda dear he lov'd,
    A maid of beauty rare,
Even Margaret on the Scottish throne
    Was never half so fair.

Lang had he woo'd, lang she refus'd
    With seeming scorn and pride ;
Yet aft her eyes confess'd the love
    Her fearful words deny'd.

At last she bless'd his well-try'd love,
    Allow'd his tender claim ;
She vow'd to him her virgin heart,
    And own'd an equal flame.

Her father, Buchan's cruel lord,
    Their passion disapprov'd,
And bade her wed Sir John the Graham,
    And leave the youth she lov'd.

[1] This line is in the sixth verse of the eighth paraphrase, known to
have been by M. Bruce.

One night they met as they were wont,
  Deep in a shady wood,
Where on the bank beside the burn
  A blooming saugh-tree stood.

Conceal'd among the underwood
  The crafty Donald lay,
The brother of Sir John the Graham,
  To list what they would say.

When thus the maid began :—My sire
  Our passion disapproves,
And bids me wed Sir John the Graham ;
  So here must end our loves !

My father's will must be obey'd,
  Nought boots me to withstand.
Some fairer maid in beautie's bloom
  Shall bless thee with her hand.

Matilda soon shall be forgot
  And from thy mind effaced,
But may that happiness be thine
  Which I can never taste.

What do I hear ? Is this thy vow ?
  Sir James the Ross reply'd.
And will Matilda wed the Graham,
  Tho' sworn to be my bride ?

His sword shall sooner pierce my heart
  Than reave me of my charms !
Then clasp'd her to his beating breast
  Fast lock'd within her arms.

I spake to try thy love, she said ;
  I'll ne'er wed man but thee ;
The grave shall be my bridal bed,
  Ere Graham my husband be.

Take then, dear youth, this faithful kiss
  In witness of my troth,
And every plague become my lot
  That day I break my oath.

They parted thus ; the sun was set.
  Up hasty Donald flies,
And turn thee, turn thee, beardless youth !
  He loud insulting cries.

Soon turn'd about the fearless chief,
  And soon his sword he drew,
For Donald's blade before his breast
  Had pierc'd his tartans through.

This for my brother's slighted love,
  His wrongs sit on my arm ;
Three paces back the youth retir'd,
  And sav'd himself frae harm.

Returning swift, his sword he rear'd
  Fierce Donald's head above,
And thro' the brain and crashing bone
  His sharp-edg'd weapon drove.

He stagg'ring reel'd, then instant fell
  A lump of lifeless clay.
So fall my foes ! quoth valiant Ross,
  And stately strode away.

Thro' the green wood in haste he pass'd
    Unto Lord Buchan's hall ;
And at Matilda's window stood,
    And thus on her did call :

Art thou asleep, Matilda dear ?
    Awake, my love, awake ;
Behold, thy lover waits without,
    A long farewell to take.

For I have slain fierce Donald Graham,
    His blood is on my sword ;
And distant are my faithful men,
    That would assist their lord.

To Skye I will direct my way,
    Where my two brothers bide,
And raise the valiant of the Isles
    To combat on my side.

O, do not so ! the maid replied.
    With me till morning stay,
For dark and dreary is the night,
    And dangerous is the way ;

All night I'll watch you in the park ;
    My faithful page I'll send
To run and raise the brave Clan Ross
    Their master to defend.

Beneath a bush he laid him down,
    Wrapt in his tartan plaid,
While, trembling for her lover's fate,
    At distance stood the maid.

Swift ran the page o'er hill and dale,
  Till in a lowly glen
He met the furious Sir John Graham,
  With twenty of his men.

Where go'st thou, little page ? he said ;
  So late who did thee send ?
I go to raise the brave Clan Ross
  Their master to defend.

For he has slain fierce Donald Graham,
  His blood is on his sword,
And far, far distant are his men
  That can assist their lord.

And has he slain my brother dear ?
  The furious Graham replies ;
Dishonour blast my name, but he
  By me ere morning dies !

Tell me, where is Sir James the Ross ?
  I will thee well reward.
He sleeps into Lord Buchan's park ;
  Matilda is his guard.

They spurr'd their steeds in furious mood
  And scour'd along the lea,
They reach'd Lord Buchan's lofty tow'rs
  By dawning of the day.

Matilda stood without the gate,
  Upon a rising ground,
And watch'd each object in the dawn,
  All ear to every sound.

Where sleeps the Ross ? began the Graham,
  Or has the felon fled ?
This hand shall lay the wretch in earth
  By whom my brother bled.

Last day at noon, Matilda said,
  Sir James the Ross pass'd by,
He furious prick'd his sweaty steed,
  And onward fast did hye.

By this he's at Edina's cross,
  If horse and man hold good.—
Your page then ly'd, who said he was
  Now sleeping in the wood.

She wrung her hands and tore her hair.
  Brave Ross ! thou art betray'd,
And ruin'd by those very means
  From whence I hop'd thine aid.

By this the valiant knight awoke ;
  The virgin's shriek he heard ;
And up he rose and drew his sword,
  When the fierce band appear'd.

Your sword last night my brother slew,
  His blood yet dims its shine,
But ere the setting of the sun
  Your blood shall reek on mine.

Your words seem brave, the chief return'd,
  But deeds approve the man ;
Set by your men, and hand to hand
  We'll try what valour can.

Oft boasting hides a coward's heart ;
   My weighty sword you fear,
Which shone in front of Flodden field
   When you kept in the rear.

With dauntless step he forward strode,
   And dar'd him to the flight ;
But Graham gave back and fear'd his arm,
   For well he knew its might.

Four of his men, the bravest four,
   Sunk down beneath his sword ;
But still he scorn'd the poor revenge,
   And sought their haughty lord.

Behind him basely came the Graham,
   And pierce'd him in the side ;
Out spouting came the purple tide,
   And all his tartans dy'd.

But yet his sword quat not the grip,
   Nor dropt he to the ground,
Till thro' his en'my's heart his steel
   Had forc'd a mortal wound.

Graham, like tree by wind o'erthrown,
   Fell lifeless on the clay,
And down beside him sunk the Ross,
   And faint and dying lay.

The sad Matilda saw him fall :
   O spare his life ! she cried.
Lord Buchan's daughter begs his life,
   Let her not be denied !

Her well-known voice the hero heard,
   He rais'd his half-clos'd eyes,
And fix'd them on the weeping maid,
   And weakly thus replies :

In vain Matilda begs the life
   By death's arrest deny'd ;
My race is run—Adieu, my love ![1]
   Then clos'd his eyes and died.

The sword, yet warm, from his left side
   With frantic hand she drew ;
I come, Sir James the Ross ! she cried,
   I come to follow you.

She lean'd the hilt against the ground,
   And bar'd her snowy breast ;
Then fell upon her lover's face,
   And sunk to endless rest.

ODE : TO A FOUNTAIN

O FOUNTAIN of the wood ! whose glassy wave,
   Slow-welling from the rock of years,
      Holds to heav'n a mirror blue,
         And bright as Anna's eye,

With whom I've sported on the margin green.
   My hand with leaves, with lilies white,
      Gaily deck'd her golden hair,
         Young Naiad of the vale.

[1] " The race appointed I have run," appears in Bruce's Hymn
No. 5 of the Paraphrases.

ODE : TO A FOUNTAIN

Fount of my native wood ! thy murmurs greet
  My ear, like poet's heavenly strain :
    Fancy pictures in a dream
      The golden days of youth.

O state of innocence ! O paradise !
  In Hope's gay garden Fancy views
    Golden blossoms, golden fruits,
      And Eden ever green.

Where now, ye dear companions of my youth !
  Ye brothers of my bosom ! where
    Do ye tread the walks of life,
      Wide scatter'd o'er the world ?

Thus wingèd larks forsake their native nest,
  The merry minstrels of the morn ;
    Now to heav'n they mount away.
      And meet again no more.

All things decay ; the forest like the leaf ;
  Great kingdoms fall ; the peopled globe,
    Planet-struck, shall pass away ;
      Heav'ns with their hosts expire :

But Hope's fair visions and the beams of Joy
  Shall cheer my bosom : I will sing
    Nature's beauty, Nature's birth,
      And heroes on the lyre.

Ye Naiads ! blue-eyed sisters of the wood ! [1]
  Who by old oak or storied stream
    Nightly tread your mystic maze,
      And charm the wand'ring Moon,

[1] In " Lochleven," page 205 :
" Beheld the blue-eyed Sisters of the stream."
This, together with the evident allusion in the third stanza to
the " Fount " called " Scotland *Well*," incidentally confirms the
Bruce authorship of this Ode.

Beheld by poet's eye ; inspire my dreams
With visions like the landscape fair,
Of heaven's bliss to dying saints
By guardian angels drawn

Fount of the forest ! in thy poet's lays
Thy waves shall flow : this wreath of flow'rs,
Gather'd by my Anna's hand,
I ask to bind my brow.

DANISH ODE

THE great, the glorious deed is done !
The foe has fled ! the field is won !
Prepare the feast, the heroes call ;
Let joy, let triumph fill the hall !

The raven claps his sable wings ;
The Bard his chosen timbrel brings ;
Six virgins round, a select choir,
Sing to the music of his lyre.

With mighty ale the goblet crown,
And herewith all your sorrows drown ;
To-day to mirth and joy we yield ;
To-morrow, face the bloody field.

From danger's front, at battle's eve
Sweet comes the banquet to the brave ;
Joy shines with genial beam on all,
The joy that dwells in Odin's hall.

The song bursts living from the lyre,
Like dreams that guardian ghosts inspire ;
When music shrieks the heroes hear,
And whirl the visionary spear.

Music's the med'cine of the mind ;
The cloud of Care give to the wind ;
Be ev'ry brow with garlands bound,
And let the cup of joy go round.

The cloud comes o'er the beam of light ;
We're guests that tarry but a night :
In the dark house, together press'd,
The princes and the people rest.

Send round the shell,[1] the feast prolong,
And send away the night in song ;
Be blest below, as those above
With Odin's and the friends they love.

DANISH ODE

In deeds of arms our fathers rise
Illustrious in their offspring's eyes ;
They fearless rush'd through Ocean's storms,
And dar'd grim Death in all its forms ;
Each youth assum'd the sword and shield,
And grew a hero in the field.

[1] The ancient Danes and Scots drank from shells. " To rejoice in the shell " is a phrase used in Ossian for drinking freely.

165

Shall we degenerate from our race,
Inglorious in the mountain chase ?
Arm, arm in fallen Hubba's right ;
Place your forefathers in your sight ;
To fame, to glory, fight your way,
And teach the nations to obey.

Assume the oars, unbind the sails ;
Send, Odin ! send propitious gales.
At Loda's stone we will adore
Thy name with songs upon the shore ;
And, full of thee, undaunted dare
The foe, and dart the bolts of war.

No feast of shells, no dance by night,
Are glorious Odin's dear delight ;
He, king of men, his armies led
Where heroes strove, where battles bled ;
Now reigns above the morning-star,
The god of thunder and of war.

Bless'd who in battle bravely fall !
They mount on wings to Odin's Hall ;
To music's sound, in cups of gold,
They drink new wine with chiefs of old ;
The song of bards records their name,
And future times shall speak their fame.

Hark ! Odin thunders ! haste on board ;
Illustrious Canute ![1] give the word.
On wings of wind we pass the seas,
To conquer realms, if Odin please :
With Odin's spirit in our soul,
We'll gain the globe from pole to pole.

[1] Canute, surnamed the Great, King of Denmark, was upon the death of Edmund proclaimed King of England, A.D. 1017.

TO PAOLI

THE CORSICAN HERO

" Paoli's father was one of the patriots who effected their escape from Corsica when the French reduced it to obedience. He retired to Naples, and brought up this, his youngest son, in the Neapolitan service. The Corsicans heard of young Paoli's abilities, and solicited him to come over to his native country and take the command. He found all things in confusion : he formed a democratical government, of which he was chosen chief, and took such measures both for repressing abuses and moulding the rising generation, that if France had not interfered, Corsica might at this day have been as free and flourishing and happy a common-wealth as any of the Grecian States in the days of their prosperity. A desperate struggle was made against the French usurpation. They offered to confirm Paoli in the supreme government, only on condition that he would hold it under their government. This he refused. They then set a price upon his head. During two campaigns he kept them at bay : they overpowered him at length ; he was driven to the shore, and having escaped on shipboard, took refuge in England."—Southey's " Life of Nelson."

It is clear to any candid mind, after a careful study of the great events which had passed and were in process of development in Corsica, that Bruce had enough of information to supply him with all that is contained in this ode. Besides, the very language and expressions used in it are to be found in Bruce's other pieces. Till 1766 the ordinary literature of the country was full of statements anent that unequal but eventful conflict, of all of which Bruce would be cognisant. In *The Gentleman's Magazine* an excellent article appeared full of particulars fitted to exhibit the case as it stood, as well as to anticipate all that happened shortly afterwards.

WHAT man, what hero shall the Muses sing,
On classic lyre or Caledonian string ?
    Whose name shall fill th' immortal page ?
Who, fir'd from heav'n with energy divine,
In sun-bright glory bids his actions shine
    First in the annals of the age ?

Ceas'd are the golden times of yore ;
The age of heroes is no more ;
Rare, in these latter times, arise to fame
The poet's strain inspir'd, or hero's heavenly flame.

What star arising in the southern sky,
New to the heav'ns, attracting Europe's eye,
    With beams unborrow'd shines afar ?
Who comes, with thousands marching in his rear,
Shining in arms, shaking his bloody spear,
    Like the red comet, sign of war ?
    Paoli ! sent of Heav'n to save
    A rising nation of the brave ;
Whose firm right hand his angels arm, to bear
A shield before his host, and dart the bolts of war.

He comes ! he comes ! the saviour of the land !
His drawn sword flames in his uplifted hand,
    Enthusiast in his country's cause ;
Whose firm resolve obeys a nation's call,
To rise deliverer, or a martyr fall
    To Liberty, to dying laws.
    Ye sons of Freedom ! sing his praise ;
    Ye poets ! bind his brows with bays ;
Ye sceptr'd shadows ! cast your honours down,
And bow before the head that never wore a crown.

Who to the hero can the palm refuse ?
Great Alexander still the world subdues,
    The heir of everlasting praise.
But when the hero's flame, the patriot's light,
When virtues human and divine unite ;
    When olives twine among the bays,
    And mutual both Minervas shine ;
    A constellation so divine
A wond'ring world behold, admire, and love,
And His best image here th' Almighty marks above.

168

As the lone shepherd hides him in the rocks,
When high heav'n thunders ; as the tim'rous flocks
    From the descending torrent flee :
So flies a world of slaves at War's alarms,
When Zeal on flame, and Liberty in arms,
    Leads on the fearless and the free,
  Resistless ; as the torrent flood,
  Horn'd like the moon, uproots the wood,
Sweeps flocks, and herds, and harvests from their base,
And moves th' eternal hills from their appointed place.

Long hast thou labour'd in the glorious strife,
O land of Liberty ! profuse of life,
    And prodigal of priceless blood.
Where heroes bought with blood the martyr's crown,
A race arose, heirs of their high renown,
    Who dar'd their fate thro' fire and flood ;
  And Gaffori[1] the great arose,
  Whose words of pow'r disarm'd his foes ;
And where the filial image smil'd afar,
The sire turned not aside the thunders of the war.

[1] " Gaffori was a hero worthy of old times. His eloquence was long remembered with admiration. A band of assassins was once advancing against him. He heard of their approach, went out to meet them, and with a serene dignity which overawed them, requested them to hear him. He then spoke to them so forcibly of the distresses of their country, her intolerable wrongs, and the hopes and views of their brethren in arms, that the very men who had been hired to murder him fell at his feet, implored his forgiveness, and joined his banners. While he was besieging the Genoese in Corte, a part of the garrison perceiving the nurse with his eldest son, then an infant in arms, straying at a little distance from the camp, suddenly sallied, and seized them. The use they made of their persons was in conformity to their usual execrable conduct. When Gaffori advanced to batter the walls, they held up the child directly over that part of the wall at which the guns were pointed. The Corsicans stopt ; but Gaffori stood at their head, and ordered them to continue the fire. Providentially the child escaped, and lived to relate, with becoming feeling, a fact so honourable to his father."—Southey's " Life of Nelson."

O Liberty ! to man a guardian giv'n,
Thou best and brightest attribute of Heav'n !
    From whom descending, thee we sing.
By nature wild, or by the arts refin'd,
We feel thy pow'r essential to our mind ;
    Each son of Freedom is a king.
    Thy praise the happy world proclaim,
    And Britain worships at thy name,
Thou guardian angel of Britannia's isle ![1]
And God and man rejoice in thy immortal smile !

Island of beauty ! lift thy head on high ;
Sing a new song of triumph to the sky !
    The day of thy deliv'rance springs !
The day of vengeance to thy ancient foe.
Thy sons shall lay the proud oppressor low,[2]
    And break the head of tyrant kings.
    Paoli ! mighty man of war !
    All bright in arms, thy conqu'ring car
Ascend ; thy people from the foe redeem,
Thou delegate of Heav'n, the son of the Supreme !

Ruled by th' eternal laws, supreme o'er all,
Kingdoms, like kings, successive rise and fall.
    When Caesar conquer'd half the earth,
And spread his eagles in Britannia's sun,
Did Caesar dream the savage huts he won
    Should give a far-famed kingdom birth ?
    That here should Roman freedom light ;
    The western Muses wing their flight ;
The Arts, the Graces, find their fav'rite home ;
Our armies awe the globe, and Britain rival Rome ?

[1] Burns adopts this in his " Cottar's Saturday Night."

[2] And this, in his " Scots wha hae."

Thus, if th' Almighty say, " Let Freedom be,"
Thou, Corsica ! thy golden age shalt see,
   Rejoice with songs, rejoice with smiles ;
Worlds yet unfound, and ages yet unborn,
Shall hail a new Britannia in her morn,
   The Queen of arts, the Queen of isles ;
  The Arts, the beauteous train of Peace,
  Shall rise and rival Rome and Greece ;
A Newton Nature's book unfold sublime ;
A Milton sing to heav'n, and charm the ear of Time !

THE EAGLE, CROW, AND SHEPHERD[1]

A FABLE

BENEATH the horror of a rock,
A shepherd careless fed his flock.
Souse from its top an eagle came,
And seiz'd upon a sporting lamb ;
Its tender sides his talons tear,
And bear it bleating thro' the air.

This was discover'd by a crow,
Who hopp'd upon the plain below.
" Yon ram," says he, " becomes my prey " ;
And, mounting, hastens to the fray ;
Lights on his back—when lo, ill-luck !
He in the fleece entangled stuck ;
He spreads his wings, but can't get free,
Struggling in vain for liberty.

The shepherd soon the captive spies,
And soon he seizes on the prize.
His children curious crowd around,
And ask what strange fowl he has found ?

[1] Written to furnish a lesson to a conceited youth at college.

" My sons," said he, " warn'd by this wretch,
Attempt no deed above your reach :
An eagle not an hour ago,
He's now content to be a crow."

THE MUSIAD : A MINOR EPIC POEM

IN THE MANNER OF HOMER. A FRAGMENT

In ancient times, ere traps were fram'd,
    Or cats in Britain's isle were known ;
A mouse, for pow'r and valour fam'd,
    Possess'd in peace the regal throne.

A farmer's house he nightly storm'd,
    (In vain were bolts, in vain were keys) ;
The milk's fair surface he deform'd,
    And digg'd entrenchments in the cheese.

In vain the farmer watch'd by night,
    In vain he spread the poison'd bacon ;
The mouse was wise as well as wight,
    Nor could by force or fraud be taken.

His subjects follow'd where he led,
    And dealt destruction all around ;
His people, shepherd-like, he fed ;
    Such mice are rarely to be found.

But evil fortune had decreed
    (The foe of mice as well as men)
The royal mouse at last should bleed,
    Should fall—ne'er to arise again.

Upon a night, as authors say,
   A luckless scent our hero drew,
Upon forbidden ground to stray,
   And pass a narrow cranny through.

That night a feast the farmer made,
   And joy unbounded fill'd the house ;
The fragments in the pantry spread
   Afforded bus'ness to the mouse.

He ate his fill, and back again
   Return'd ; but access was deny'd.
He search'd each corner, but in vain
   He found it close on every side.

Let none our hero's fears deride ;
   He roar'd (ten mice of modern days,
As mice are dwindl'd and decay'd,
   So great a voice could scarcely raise).

Rous'd at the voice the farmer ran,
   And seiz'd upon his hapless prey.
With entreaties the mouse began,
   And pray'rs his anger to allay.

" O spare my life ! " he trembling cries ;
   " My subjects will a ransom give
Large as thy wishes can devise,
   Soon as it shall be heard I live."

" No, wretch ! " the farmer says in wrath,
   " Thou dy'st ; no ransom I'll receive."
" My subjects will revenge my death,"
   He said, " this dying charge I leave."

The farmer lifts his armèd hand,
　And on the mouse inflicts a wound.
What mouse could such a blow withstand ?
　He fell, and dying bit the ground.

Thus Lambris fell, who flourish'd long
　(I half forgot to tell his name);
But his renown lives in the song,
　And future times shall speak his fame.

A mouse who walk'd about at large
　In safety heard his mournful cries ;
He heard him give his dying charge,
　And to the rest he frantic flies.

Thrice he essay'd to speak, and thrice
　Tears, such as mice may shed, fell down
" Revenge your monarch's death !" he cries,
　His voice half-stifl'd with a groan.

But having re-assumed his senses
　And reason, such as mice may have,
He told out all the circumstances
　With many a strain and broken heave.

Chill'd with sad grief, th' assembly heard ;
　Each dropp'd a tear, and bow'd the head :
But symptoms soon of rage appear'd,
　And vengeance for their royal dead.

Long sat they mute : at last up rose
　The great Hypenor, blameless sage !
A hero born to many woes ;
　His head was silver'd o'er with age.

His bulk so large, his joints so strong,
　　Though worn with grief, and past his prime,
Few rats could equal him, 'tis sung,
　　As rats are in these dregs of time.

Two sons, in battle brave, he had,
　　Sprung from fair Lalage's embrace ;
Short time they grac'd his nuptial bed,
　　By dogs destroy'd in cruel chase.

Their timeless fate the mother wailed,
　　And pined with heart-corroding grief :
O'er every comfort it prevail'd,
　　Till death advancing brought relief.

Now he's the last of all his race,
　　A prey to woe he inly pined ;
Grief pictur'd sat upon his face ;
　　Upon his breast his head reclin'd.

And, " O my fellow-mice ! " he said,
　　" These eyes ne'er saw a day so dire,
Save when my gallant children bled.
　　O wretched sons ! O wretched sire !

" But now a general cause demands
　　Our grief, and claims our tears alone ;
Our monarch, slain by wicked hands,
　　No issue left to fill the throne.

" Yet tho' by hostile man much wrong'd,
　　My counsel is, from arms forbear,
That so your days may be prolonged ;
　　For man is Heaven's peculiar care."

ANACREONTIC : TO A WASP

The following is a ludicrous imitation of the usual Anacreontics ; the spirit of composing which was raging, a few years ago, among all the sweet singers of Great Britain.

WINGÈD wanderer of the sky !
Inhabitant of heaven high !
Dreadful with thy dragon-tail,
Hydra-head, and coat of mail !
Why dost thou my peace molest ?
Why dost thou disturb my rest ?
When in May the meads are seen,
Sweet enamel ! white and green ;
And the gardens, and the bowers,
And the forests, and the flowers,
Don their robes of curious dye,
Fine confusion to the eye ;
Did I, chase thee in thy light ?
Did I, put thee in a fright ?
Did I, spoil thy treasure hid ?
Never, never, never, did.
Envious nothing ! pray beware ;
Tempt mine anger, if you dare.
Trust not in thy strength of wing ;
Trust not in thy length of sting.
Heaven nor earth shall thee defend ;
I thy buzzing soon will end.
Take my counsel, while you may ;
Devil take you if you stay.
Wilt, thou, dare, my, face, to, wound ?—
Thus I fell thee to the ground.

Down amongst the dead men, now
Thou shalt forget thou ere wast thou.
Anacreontic Bards beneath,
Thus shall wail thee after death.

CHORUS OF ELYSIAN BARDS

A Wasp, for a wonder,
To paradise under
Descends. See ! he wanders
By Styx's meanders !
Behold how he glows
Amidst Rhodope's snows ;
He sweats, in a trice,
In the regions of ice !
Lo ! he cools, by God's ire,
Amidst brimstone and fire !
He goes to our King,
And he shows him his sting ;
(God Pluto loves satire,
As women love attire);
Our King sets him free,
Like fam'd Eurydice.

Thus a wasp could prevail
O'er the Devil and hell,
A conquest both hard and laborious !
Tho' hell had fast bound him,
And the Devil did confound him,
Yet his sting and his wing were victorious.

ALEXIS[1]

A PASTORAL

Upon a bank with cowslips covered o'er,
Where Leven's waters break against the shore ;
What time the village sires in circles talk,
And youths and maidens take their evening walk ;
Among the yellow broom Alexis lay,
And viewed the beauties of the setting day.

Full well you might observe some inward smart,
Some secret grief hung heavy at his heart.
While round the field his sportive lambkins play'd,
He rais'd his plaintive voice, and thus he said :

Begin, my pipe ! a softly mournful strain.
The parting sun shines yellow on the plain ;
The balmy west wind breathes along the ground ;
Their evening sweets the flow'rs dispense around ;
The flocks stray bleating o'er the mountain's brow,
And from the plain the answ'ring cattle low ;
Sweet chant the feather'd tribes on every tree,
And all things feel the joys of love, but me.

Begin, my pipe ! begin the mournful strain.
Eumelia meets my kindness with disdain.[2]
Oft have I try'd her stubborn heart to move,
    And in her icy bosom kindle love :
But all in vain—ere I my love declared,
With other youths her company I shar'd ;
But now she shuns me hopeless and forlorn,
And pays my constant passion with her scorn.

[1] Bruce here refers to himself.

[2] Also mentioned in the " Vernal Ode " and refers to his favourite
" Peggy," Margaret White of Kinnesswood.

Begin, my pipe ! the sadly-soothing strain
And bring the days of innocence again.
Well I remember, in the sunny scene
We ran, we played together on the green.
Fair in our youth, and wanton in our play,
We toyed, we sported the long summer's day.
For her I spoil'd the gardens of the Spring,
And taught the goldfinch on her hand to sing.
We sat and sung beneath the lovers' tree ;
One was her look, and it was fixed on me.

Begin, my pipe ! a melancholy strain.
A holiday was kept on yonder plain ;
The feast was spread upon the flowery mead,
And skilful Thyrsis tuned his vocal reed ;
Each for the dance selects the nymph he loves,
And every nymph with smiles her swain approves :
The setting sun beheld their mirthful glee,
And left all happy in their love—but me.

Begin, my pipe ! a softly mournful strain.
O cruel nymph ! O most unhappy swain !
To climb the steepy rock's tremendous height
And crop its herbage is the goat's delight ;
The flowery thyme delights the humming bees,
And blooming wilds the bleating lambkins please ;
Daphnis[1] courts Chloe under every tree :
Eumelia ! you alone have joys for me !

Now cease, my pipe ! now cease the mournful strain.
Lo, yonder comes Eumelia o'er the plain !
Till she approach, I'll lurk behind the shade,
Then try with all my art the stubborn maid :

[1] Willie Arnot, his friend.

Though to her lover cruel and unkind,
Yet time may change the purpose of her mind.
But vain these pleasing hopes ! already see,
She hath observ'd, and now she flies from me !

Then cease, my pipe ! the unavailing strain.
Apollo aids, the Nine inspire, in vain :
You cruel maid ! refuse to lend an ear ;
No more I sing, since you disdain to hear.
This pipe Amyntas[1] gave, on which he play'd :
" Be thou its second lord," the dying shepherd said.
No more I play, now silent let it be ;
Nor pipe, nor song, can e'er give joy to me.

DAMON, MENALCAS, AND MELIBŒUS [2]

AN ECLOGUE

DAMON

MILD from the shower, the morning's rosy light
Unfolds the beauteous season to the sight :
The landscape rises verdant on the view ;
The little hills uplift their heads in dew ;
The sunny stream rejoices in the vale ;
The woods with songs approaching summer hail :
The boy comes forth among the flow'rs to play ;
His fair hair glitters in the yellow ray.
Shepherds, begin the song ! while, o'er the mead
Your flocks at will on dewy pastures feed.
Behold fair nature, and begin the song ;
The songs of nature to the swain belong.

[1] Pseudonym assumed by Bruce.
[2] Pseudonyms assumed by James Bruce and his friends.

Who equals Cona's bard in sylvan strains,
To him his harp an equal prize remains ;
His harp, which sounds on all its sacred strings
The loves of hunters, and the wars of kings.

MENALCAS

Now fleecy clouds in clearer skies are seen ;
The air is genial, and the earth is green :
O'er hill and dale the flowers spontaneous spring,
And blackbirds singing now invite to sing.

MELIBŒUS

Now milky showers rejoice the springing grain ;
New-opening pea-blooms purple all the plain ;
The hedges blossom white on every hand ;
Already harvest seems to clothe the land.

MENALCAS

White o'er the hill my snowy sheep appear,
Each with her lamb ; their shepherd's name they bear.
I love to lead them where the daisies spring,
And on the sunny hill to sit and sing.

MELIBŒUS

My fields are green with clover and with corn ;
My flocks the hills, and herds the vales, adorn,
I teach the stream, I teach the vocal shore,
And woods, to echo that " I want no more."

MENALCAS

To me the bees their annual nectar yield ;
Peace cheers my hut, and plenty clothes my field.
I fear no loss : I give to Ocean's wind
All care away, a monarch in my mind.

Meliboeus

My mind is cheerful as the linnet's lays ;
Heaven daily hears a shepherd's simple praise.
What time I shear my flock I send a fleece
To aged Mopsa and her orphan niece.

Menalcas

Levinia, come ! here primroses upspring ;
Here choirs of linnets, here yourself may sing ;
Here meadows worthy of thy foot appear :
O come, Levinia ! let us wander here ![1]

Meliboeus

Rosella, come ! here flow'rs the heath adorn ;
Here ruddy roses open on the thorn ;
Here willows by the brook a shadow give ;
O here, Rosella ! let us love to live.

Menalcas

Levinia's fairer than the flow'rs of May,
Or Autumn apples ruddy in the ray :
For her my flowers are in a garland wove,
And all my apples ripen for my love.

Meliboeus

Prince of the wood, the oak majestic tow rs ;
The lily of the vale is queen of flow'rs[2] :
Above the maids Rosella's charms prevail,
As oaks in woods, and lilies in the vale !

[1] These four lines were written by Logan.

[2] As in Bruce's " Lochleven."

MENALCAS

Resound, ye rocks ! ye little hills, rejoice !
Assenting woods, to Heaven uplift your voice !
Let Spring and Summer enter hand in hand ;
Levinia comes, the glory of our Land !

MELIBŒUS

Whene'er my love appears upon the plain,
To her the wond'ring shepherds tune the strain :
" Who comes in beauty like the vernal morn,
When yellow robes of light all heaven and earth
    adorn."

MENALCAS

Rosella's mine by all the Pow'rs above ;
Each star in heav'n is witness to our love.
Among the lilies she abides all day ;
Herself as lovely and as sweet as they.

MELIBŒUS

By Leven's bank Levinia feeds her flocks,
And in the sunshine combs her yellow locks.
Be thine the peace of Heav'n unknown to kings
And o'er thee angels spread their guardian wings !

MENALCAS

I followed Nature, and was fond of praise ;
Thrice noble Varro has approved my lays[1] ;
If he approves, superior to my peers
I join th' immortal choir and sing to other years.

[1] Varro in this line refers to John Birrell.

MELIBŒUS

My mistress is my Muse : the banks of Tyne
Resound with Nature's music, and with mine ;
Peggie the fair,[1] the beauty of our green,
To me adjudg'd the prize when chosen queen.

DAMON

Now cease your songs : the flocks to shelter fly,
And the high sun has gain'd the middle sky.
To both alike the poet's bays belong,
Chiefs of the choir, and masters of the song.
Thus let your pipes contend, with rival strife,
To sing the praises of the pastoral life :
Sing Nature's scenes with Nature's beauties fir'd ;
Where poets dream'd, where prophets lay inspir'd.
E'en Caledonian queens have trod the meads,
And sceptr'd kings assum'd the shepherd's weeds :
Th' angelic choirs, that guard the throne of God,
Have sat with shepherds on the humble sod.
With us renew'd the golden times remain,
And long-lost innocence is found again.

———————

PHILOCLES

An elegy on the death of his friend Mr. William Dryburgh, of
Dysart, a fellow-student.

WAILING, I sit on Leven's sandy shore,
    And sadly tune the reed to sounds of woe ;
Once more I call Melpomene ! once more
    Spontaneous teach the weeping verse to flow !

[1] Bruce's favourite, as in the " Pastoral Song."

The weeping verse shall flow in friendship's name,
  Which friendship asks, and friendship fain would
      pay ;
The weeping verse, which worth and genius claim.
  Begin then, Muse ! begin thy mournful lay.

Aided by thee I'll twine a rustic wreath
  Of fairest flow'rs, to deck the grass-grown grave
Of Philocles, cold in the bed of death,
  And mourn the gentle youth I could not save.

Where lordly Forth divides the fertile plains
  With ample sweep, a sea from side to side,
A rocky bound his raging course restrains,
  For ever lashed by the resounding tide.

There stands his tomb upon the sea-bent shore.
  Afar discerned by the rough sailor's eye,
Who passing weeps, and stops the sounding oar,
  And points where piety and virtue lie.

Like the gay palm on Rabbah's fair domains,
  Or cedar shadowing Carmel's flowery side ;
Or like the upright ash on Britain's plains,
  Which waves its stately arms in youthful pride :

So flourished Philocles : and as the hand
  Of ruthless woodman lays their honours low,
He fell in youth's fair bloom by fate's command.
  'Twas fate that struck, 'tis ours to mourn the blow.

Alas ! we fondly thought that Heaven designed
  His bright example mankind to improve :
All they should be was pictured in his mind ;
  His thoughts were virtue, and his heart was love.

Calm as a summer's sun's unruffled face,
  He looked unmoved on life's precarious game,
And smiled at mortals toiling in the chase
  Of empty phantoms—opulence and fame.

Steady he followed Virtue's onward path,
  Inflexible to Error's devious way ;
And firm at last in hope and fixed faith,
  Thro' Death's dark vale he trod without dismay.

The gloomy vale he trod, relentless Death !
  Where waste and horrid desolation reign.
The tyrant, humbled, there resigns his wrath ;
  The wretch, elated, there forgets his pain ;

There sleep the infant and the hoary head ;
  Together like the oppressor and the oppressed ;
There dwells the captive, free among the dead ;
  There Philocles, and there the weary, rest.

The curtains of the grave fast drawn around,
  Till the loud trumpet wakes the sleep of death,
With dreadful clangour through the world resound,
  Shake the firm globe, and burst the vaults beneath.

Then Philocles shall rise, to glory rise,
  And his Redeemer for himself shall see ;
With Him in triumph mount the azure skies :
  For where He is, His followers shall be.

Whence then these sighs ? and whence this falling
      tear ?
  To sad remembrance of his merit just,
Still must I mourn ; for he to me was dear,
  And still is dear, though buried in the dust.

DAPHNIS : A MONODY

To the memory of Mr. William Arnot, son of Mr. David Arnot,
laird of Portmoak.

No more of youthful joys, or love's fond dreams ;
No more of morning fair, or ev'ning mild ;
While Daphnis lies among the silent dead
Unsung ; though long ago he trode the path,
The weary road to death,
Which soon or late each human foot must tread.
He trode the dark uncomfortable wild
By Faith's light, and Truth's unsullied beams ;
By Love, whose image gladdens mortal eyes,
And keeps the golden key that opens all the skies.

Assist, ye Muses !—and ye will assist :
For Daphnis, whom I sing, to you was dear :
Ye loved the boy, and on his youthful head
Your kindest influence shed.—
So may I match his lays, who to the lyre
Wailed his lost Lycidas by wood and rill :
So may the Muse my grov'ling mind inspire
With high poetic fire ;
As thy sad loss, dear youth, with grief do (I deplore),
To sing a farewell to thy ashes blest[1] ;
To bid fair peace to be thy gentle shade ;
To scatter flowerets, cropt by Fancy's hand,
In sad assemblage round thy tomb,
If watered by the Muse, to latest time to bloom.

[1] This line and the following four are not in the MS. as sent to
Mr. Arnot senior. Yet this may have been changed when Bruce was
rewriting the piece for the printer in his MS. book.

Oft by the side of Leven's crystal Lake,
Trembling beneath the closing lids of light,
With slow short-measured steps we took our walk :
Then the dear youth would talk
Of argument far far above his years,
Or young compeers,
And high would reason ; he could reason high ;
Till from the east the silver Queen of Night
Her journey up heaven's steep began to make,
And silence reigned attentive in the sky.

O happy days !—for ever, ever gone !
When o'er the flow'ry green we ran, we play'd
With blooms bedropt by youthful Summers' hand :
Or, in the willow shade,
Upon the echoing banks of the fair Lake
We mimic castles built among the sand,
Soon by the sounding surge to be beat down,
Or sweeping wind ; when by the sedgy marsh
Or rushy pool we wand'red in our play,
And heard the heron and the wild duck harsh,
Or sweeter lark tune her melodious lay,
At highest noon of day.
Among the antic moss-grown stones we'd roam,
With ancient hieroglyphic figures wrought ;
Winged hour-glasses, bones, and spades, and skulls,
And obsolete inscriptions, by the hands
Of other years. Ay me ! I little thought
That where we play'd he soon would fill a tomb.

Where were ye, Muses ! when the leaden hand
Of Death remorseless clos'd your Daphnis' eyes ?
For sure ye heard the weeping mother's cries ;—
But the dread pow'r of Fate what can withstand ?

Young Daphnis smil'd at Death ; the tyrant's darts
As stubble counted. What was his support ?
His conscience and firm trust in Him whose ways
Are truth ; in Him who sways
His potent sceptre o'er the dark domain
Of death and hell ; who holds in straighten'd rein
Their banded legions. " Thro' the darksome vale
He'll guide my steps ; He will my heart sustain ;
I trust His plighted word, it will not fail ;
I see the dawning of immortal day ! "
He smiling said, and died !

Hail and farewell, blest youth ! Soon hast thou left
This evil world. Short was thy thread of life ;
And quickly by the envious Sisters shorn.
Thus have I seen a rose with rising morn
Unfold its fragrant bloom, sweet to the smell,
And lovely to the eye ; when a keen wind
Has tore its leaves, and laid its green head low,
Stript of its sweets : ev'n so,
So Daphnis fell ! long ere his prime he fell !
Nor left he on these plains his peer behind ;
These plains that mourn their loss, of him bereft,
No more look gay, but desert and forlorn.
No song is heard, mute is the sylvan strife.

Now cease your lamentations, shepherds, cease !
Though Daphnis died below, he lives above ;
A better life, and in a fairer clime,
Now lives. No sorrow enters that blest place ;
But songs of love and joy for ay resound ;
And music floats around,
By fanning zephyrs from the spicy groves
And flowers immortal wafted ; asphodel
And amaranth, unfading, deck the ground

With fairer colours than, ere Adam fell,
In Eden bloomed. There, haply he may hear
This artless song. Ye powers of verse ! improve
And make it worthy of your darling's ear,
And make it equal to the shepherd's love.

Thus, in the shadow of a frowning rock,
Beneath a mountain's side, shaggy and hoar,
A homely swain, tending his little flock,
Tun'd to the Doric reed his rural lay,
Rude and unletter'd in the Muse's lore,
Till in the west sunk the descending day ;
Then rising, homeward slowly held his way.

VERSES

On the death of the Rev. Wm. M'Ewen, of Dundee, a popular young minister and author, who died suddenly, at Leith.

M'EWEN gone ! and shall the mournful Muse
A tear unto his memory refuse ?
Forbid it, all ye powers that guard the just,
Your care his actions, and his life your trust.
The righteous perish ! is M'Ewen dead ?
In him Religion, Virtue's friend, is fled.
Modest in strife, bold in religion's cause,
He sought true honour in his God's applause.
What manly beauties in his works appear,
Close without straining, and concise though clear.
Though short his life, not so his deathless fame,
Succeeding ages shall revere his name.

Hail , blest immortal, hail ! while we are tost,
Thy happy soul is landed on the coast,
That land of bliss, where on the peaceful shore
Thou view'st with pleasure all thy dangers o'er ;
Lain in the silent grave, thy honour'd dust
Expects the resurrection of the just.

TO SURGEON MILLAR, M.D.[1]

On recovery from a dangerous fit of illness—written in the name
of Mr. David Pearson.

A RUSTIC youth (he seeks no better name)
Alike unknown to fortune and to fame,
Acknowledging a debt he ne'er can pay,
For thee, O Millar ! frames the artless lay :
That yet he lives, that vital warmth remains,
And life's red tide bounds briskly thro' his veins ;
To thee he owes.   His grateful heart believe,
And take his thanks sincere : 'tis all he has to give.

AN EPIGRAM

WITH Celia talking, Pray, says I,
    Think you you could a husband want ;
Or would you rather choose to die
    If Heav'n the blessing should not grant ?

[1] Dr. Millar was a surgeon in Kirkcaldy, whence he had come re-
peatedly to visit David Pearson, whose poverty prevented him from
giving the skilful physician his well-earned remuneration.   Pearson
applied to his friend Bruce to express his acknowledgments in verse,
which he did.   The above is only a small part of the letter of thanks
taken down by Mr. Birrell, as Pearson was able to repeat it.

Awhile the beauteous maid look'd down
　　Then with a blush she thus began :
" Life is a precious thing I own,
　　But what is life—without a man ?

PASTORAL SONG

TO THE TUNE OF " THE YELLOW-HAIR'D LADDIE "

In May when the gowans appear on the green ;
And flowers in the field and the forest are seen ;
Where lilies bloom bonny, and the hawthorn springs,
The yellow-hair'd laddie oft whistles and sings.

But neither the shades, nor the sweets of the flowers,
Nor the blackbirds that warbled on blossoming bow'rs,
Could pleasure his eye, or his ear entertain ;
For love was his pleasure, and love was his pain.

The shepherd thus sung, while his flocks all around
Drew nearer and nearer, and sigh'd to the sound :
Around as in chains lay the beasts of the wood,
With pity disarmèd, with music subdu'd.

Young Jessy is fair as the spring's early flower,
And Mary sings sweet as the bird in her bower ;
But *Peggy* is fairer and sweeter than they ;
With looks like the morning, with smiles like the day.

In the flower of her youth, in the bloom of eighteen,
Of virtue the goddess, of beauty the queen[1] :
One hour in her presence an era excels
Amid courts, where ambition with misery dwells.

Fair to the shepherd the new-springing flow'rs,
When May and when morning lead on the gay hours :
But Peggy is brighter and fairer than they ;
She's fair as the morning, and lovely as May.

Sweet to the shepherd the wild woodland sound,
When larks sing above him, and lambs bleat around ;
But Peggy far sweeter can speak and can sing
Than the notes of the warblers that welcome the
Spring.

When in beauty she moves by the brook of the
plain,
You would call her a Venus new sprung from the
main :
When she sings, and the woods with their echoes
reply,
You would think that an angel was warbling on high.

Ye Pow'rs that preside over mortal estate !
Whose nod ruleth Nature, whose pleasure is fate ;
O grant me, O grant me, the heav'n of her charms !
May I live in her presence, and die in her arms !

[1] Peggy here mentioned is Margaret White, his faithful companion,
residing with her father at Kinnesswood. Also mentioned in " Lochleven no More," etc.

LOCHLEVEN NO MORE

TO THE TUNE OF " LOCHABER NO MORE "

FAREWELL to Lochleven and Gairney's fair stream,
How sweet, on its banks, of my Peggy to dream ;
But now I must go to a far distant shore,
And I'll may-be return to Lochleven no more.

No more in the Spring shall I walk with my dear,
Where gowans bloom bonny, and Gairney runs clear ;
Far hence must I wander, my pleasures are o'er,
Since I'll see my dear maid and Lochleven no more.

No more do I sing, since far from my delight,
But in sighs spend the day, and in tears the long night ;
By Devon's dull current stretch'd mourning I'll lie,
While the hills and the woods to my mourning reply.

But wherever I wander, by night or by day,
True love to my Peggy still with me shall stay ;
And ever and aye my loss I'll deplore,
Till the woodlands re-echo Lochleven no more.

Though from her far distant, to her I'll be true,
And still my fond heart keep her image in view :
O could I obtain her, my grief's were all o'er,
I would mourn the dear maid and Lochleven no more.

But if Fate has decreed that it ne'er shall be so,
Then grief shall attend me wherever I go :
Till from life's stormy sea I reach death's silent shore,
Then I'll think upon her and Lochleven no more.

FRAGMENTS OF SATIRE

There was a piece entitled " Fungus." Mr. Mackenzie had reason to believe that there were a number of satires ; for, on a slip of paper in his possession, there was this note in the poet's handwriting : "Add to Satire first " ; and then these lines follow :

Or shall we weep, or grow into the spleen,
Or shall we laugh at the fantastic scene.
To see a dull mechanic, in a fit,
Throw down his plane, and strive to be a wit.
Thus wrote De Foe, a tedious length of years,
And bravely lost his conscience and his ears,

To see a priest eke out the great design,
And tug with Latin points the halting line.
Who would not laugh if two such men there were ?
Such there have been—I don't say such there are.

II

Last week I made a visit to Portmoak, the parish where I was born, and being accidentally at the funeral of an aged rustic, I was invited to partake of the usual entertainment before the interment. We were conducted into a large barn, and placed almost in a square,

When lo ! a mortal, bulky, grave, and dull,
The mighty master of the sevenfold skull,
Arose like Ajax. In the midst he stands—
A well filled bicker loads his trembling hands.
To one he comes, assumes a visage new—
" Come ask a blessing, John ?—'tis put on you."
" Bid Mungo say," says John, with half a face,
Famed for his length of beard and length of grace.

Thus have I seen, beneath a hollow rock,
A shepherd hunt his dogs among his flock—
" Run collie, Battie, Venture." Not one hears,
Then rising, runs himself, and running swears.

In short, Sir, as I have not time to poetise, the grace
is said, the drink goes round, the tobacco pipes are
lighted, and, from a cloud of smoke, a hoary-headed
rustic addressed the company thus :—" Weel, John (*i.e.*
the deceased), noo when he's gone, was a good, sensible
man, stout, and healthy, and hale ; and had the best
hand for casting peats of onybody in this kintra side.
Aweel, Sirs, we maun a' dee—Here's to ye." I was struck
with the speech of this honest man, especially with his
heroic application of the glass, in dispelling the gloomy
thoughts of death.

THE FALL OF THE TABLE

The poet's petition to Mr. Flockhart, the worthy laird of Anna
frech, who looked after the schoolhouse.

WITHIN this school a table once there stood—
It was not iron—No ! 'twas rotten wood.
Four generations it on earth had seen—
A ship's old planks composed the huge machine.
Perhaps that ship in which Columbus hurl'd
Saw other stars rise on another world,—
Or that which bore, along the dark profound,
From pole to pole, the valiant Drake around.—
Tho' miracles long since were said to cease,
Three weeks—thrice seven long days—it stood in peace ;

Upon the fourth, a warm debate arose,
Managed by words and more emphatic blows ;
The routed party to the table fled,
Which seemed to offer a defensive shade.
Thus, in the town, I've seen, when rains descend,
Where archèd porticoes their shades extend,
Papists and gifted Quakers, Tories, Whigs,
Forget their feuds, and join to save their wigs—
Men born in India, men in Europe bred,
Commence acquaintance in a mason s shed.
Thus they ensconc'd beneath the table lay,
With shouts the victors rush upon the prey,—
Attack'd the rampart where they shelter took.
With firing battered, and with engines shook,
It fell. The mighty ruins strew the ground.
It fell ! The mountains tremble at the sound.
But to what end (say you) this trifling tale ?
Perhaps, sir, man as well as wood is frail.
Perhaps his life can little more supply,
" Than just to look about us and to die."

GAIRNIE BRIDGE,
   June 17, 1765.

ECLOGUE

IN THE MANNER OF OSSIAN

O come my love ! from thy echoing hill ; thy locks on the mountain wind !

The hill-top flames with setting light ; the vale is bright with the beam of eve. Blithe on the village green the maiden milks her cows. The boy shouts in the wood, and wonders who talks from the trees. But Echo talks from the trees, repeating his notes of joy. Where art thou, O Morna ! thou fairest among women ? I hear not the bleating of thy flock, nor thy voice in the wind of the hill. Here is the field of our loves ; now is the hour of thy promise. See, frequent from the harvest-field the reapers eye the setting sun : but thou appearest not on the plain.

Daughters of the bow! Saw ye my love, with her little flock tripping before her ? Saw ye her, fair moving over the heath, and waving her locks behind like the yellow sun-beams of evening ?

Come from the hill of clouds, fair dweller of woody Lumon !

I was a boy when I went to Lumon's lovely vale. Sporting among the willows of the brook, I saw the daughters of the plain. Fair were their faces of youth ; but mine eye was fixed on Morna. Red was her cheek, and fair her hair. Her hand was white as the lily. Mild was the beam of her blue eye, and lovely as the last smile of the sun. Her eye met mine in silence. Sweet were our words together in secret. I little knew what meant the heavings of my bosom, and the wild wish of my heart. I often looked back upon Lumon's vale, and blest the fair dwelling of Morna. Her name dwelt ever on my lip. She came to my dream by night. Thou didst come in thy beauty, O maid ! lovely as the ghost of Malvina, when, clad with the robes of heaven, she came to the vale of the Moon, to visit the aged eyes of Ossian king of harps.

Come from the cloud of night, thou first of our maidens ! Come—
The wind is down ; the sky is clear : red is the cloud of evening. In circles the bat wheels over head ; the boy

pursues his flight. The farmer hails the signs of heaven, the promise of halcyon days : Joy brightens in his eyes. O Morna ! first of maidens ! thou art the joy of Salgar ! thou art his one desire ! I wait thy coming on the field. Mine eye is over all the plain. One echo spreads on every side. It is the shout of the shepherds folding their flocks They call to their companions, each on his echoing hill. From the red cloud rises, the evening star.—But who comes yonder in light, like the Moon the queen of heaven ? It is she ! the star of stars ! the lovely light of Lumon ! Welcome, fair beam of beauty, for ever to shine in our valleys.

MORNA

I come from the hill of clouds. Among the green rushes of Balva's bank. I follow the steps of my beloved. The foal in the meadow frolics round the mare : his bright mane dances on the mountain wind. The leverets play among the green ferns, fearless of the hunter's horn, and of the bounding grey-hound. The last strain is up in the wood.—Did I hear the voice of my love ? It was the gale that sports with the whirling leaf, and sighs in the reeds of the lake. Blessed be the voice of winds that brings my Salgar to mind. O Salgar ! youth of the rolling eye ! thou art the love of the maidens. Thy face is a sun to thy friends : thy words are sweet as a song : thy steps are stately on thy hill : thou art comely in the brightness of youth ; like the Moon, when she puts off her dun robe in the sky, and brightens the face of night. The clouds rejoice on either side : the traveller in the narrow path beholds her, round, in her beauty moving through the midst of heaven. Thou art fair, O youth of the rolling eye ! thou wast the love of my youth.

SALGAR

Fair wanderer of evening ! pleasant be thy rest on our plains. I was gathering nuts in the wood for my love, and the days of our youth returned to mind ; when we played together on the green, and flew over the field with feet of wind. I tamed the blackbird for my love, and taught it to sing in her hand. I climbed the ash in the cliff of the rock, and brought you the doves of the wood.

MORNA

It is the voice of my beloved ! Let me behold him from the wood-covered vale, as he sings of the times of old, and complains to the voice of the rock. Pleasant were the days of our youth, like the songs of other years. Often have we sat on the old grey stone, and silent marked the stars, as one by one they stole into the sky. One was our wish by day, and one our dream by night.

SALGAR

I found an apple-tree in the wood. I planted it in my garden. Thine eye beheld it all in flower. For every bloom we marked, I count an apple of gold. To-morrow I pull the fruit for you. O come, my best beloved.

MORNA

When the gossamer melts in air and the furze crackle in the beam of moon, O come to Cona's sunny side, and let thy flocks wander in our valleys. The heath is in flower. One tree rises in the midst. Sweet flows the river by its side of age. The wild bee hides his honey at its root. Our words will be sweet on the sunny hill. Till grey evening shadow the plain, I will sing to my well-beloved.

THE VANITY OF OUR DESIRE OF IMMORTALITY HERE

A STORY IN THE EASTERN MANNER

CHILD of the years to come attend to the words of Calem ;—Calem, who hath seen fourteen kings upon the throne of China, whose days are a thousand four hundred and thirty-nine years.

Thou, O young man ! who rejoicest in thy vigour ; the days of my strength were as thine. My possessions were large, and fair as the gardens of Paradise. My cattle covered the vallies ; and my flocks were as the grass on Mount Tirza. Gold was brought me from the ocean, and jewels from the Valley of Serpents. Yet I was unhappy ; for I feared the sword of the angel of Death.

One day, as I was walking through the woods which grew around my palace, I heard the song of the birds : but I heard it without joy. On the contrary, their cheerfulness filled me with melancholy. I threw myself on a bank of flowers, and gave vent to my discontent in these words : " The time of the singing of birds is come, and the voice of the turtle is heard. These trees spread their verdant branches above me, and beneath the flowers bloom fair. The whole creation rejoices in its existence. I alone am unhappy. Why am I unhappy ? What do I want ? Nothing. But what avail my riches, when in a little I must leave them ? What is the life of man ? His days are but a thousand years ! As the waves of the ocean ; such are the generations of man : The foremost is dashed on the shore, and another comes rolling on. As the leaves of a tree ; so are the children of men :

They are scattered abroad by the wind, and other leaves lift their green heads. So the generations before us are gone ; this shall pass away; and another race arise. How, then, can I be glad, when in a few centuries I shall be no more ? Thou Eternal, why hast thou cut off the life of man ? and why are his days so few ? "

I held my peace. Immediately the sky was black with the clouds of night. A tempest shook the trees of the forest : the thunder roared from the top of Tirza, and the red bolt shot through the darkness. Terror and amazement seized me ; and the hand of him before whom the sun is extinguished, was upon me. " Calem," said he (while my bones trembled), " I have heard thee accusing me. Thou desirest life ; enjoy it. I have commanded Death that he touch thee not."

Again the clouds dispersed ; and the sun chased the shadows along the hills. The birds renewed their song, sweeter than ever before I had heard them. I cast mine eyes over my fields, while my heart exulted with joy. " These," said I, " are mine for ever ! " But I knew not that sorrow waited for me.

As I was returning home, I met the beautiful Selima walking across the fields. The rose blushed in her cheeks ; and her eyes were as the stars of the morning. Never before had I looked with a partial eye on woman. I gazed ; I sighed ; I trembled. I led her to my house, and made her mistress of my riches.

As the young plants grew up around the cedar ; so my children grew up in my hall.

Now my happiness was complete. My children married, and I saw my descendants in the third generation. I expected to see them overspread the kingdom, and that I should obtain the crown of China.

I had now lived a thousand years ; and the hand of time had withered my strength. My wife, my sons, and my daughters, died ; and I was a stranger among my people. I was a burden to them ; they hated me, and drove me from my house. Naked and miserable, I wandered ; my tottering legs scarce supported my body. I went to the dwellings of my friends ; but they were gone, and other masters chid me from their doors. I retired to the woods ; and, in a cave, lived with the beasts of the earth. Berries and roots were my meat ; and I drank of the stream of the rock. I was scorched with the summer's sun ; and shivered in the cold of winter. I was weary of life.

One day I wandered from the woods, to view the palace which was once mine. I saw it ; but it was low. Fire had consumed it : It lay as a rock cast down by an earthquake. Nettles sprung up in the court ; and from within the owl scream'd hideous. The fox looked out at the window : the rank grass of the wall waved around his head. I was filled with grief at the remembrance of what it, and what I had been. " Cursed be the day," I said, " in which I desired to live for ever. And why, O Thou Supreme ! didst Thou grant my request ? Had it not been for this, I had been at peace ; I had been asleep in the quiet grave ; I had not known the desolation of my inheritance ; I had been free from the weariness of life. I seek for death, but I find it not : my life is a curse unto me."

A shining cloud descended on the trees ; and Gabriel the angel stood before me. His voice was as the roaring stream, while thus he declared his message : " Thus saith the Highest, What shall I do unto thee, O Calem ? What dost thou now desire ? Thou askedst life, and I gave it thee, even to live for ever. Now thou art weary of living ; and again thou hast opened thy mouth against me."

THE BRAES OF YARROW

(A variation of the old ballad " The Dowie Dens of Yarrow ")

THY braes were bonny, Yarrow stream !
   When first on them I met my lover ;
Thy braes how dreary, Yarrow stream !
   When now thy waves his body cover !
For ever now, O Yarrow stream !
   Thou art to me a stream of sorrow ;
For never on thy banks shall I
   Behold my love, the flower of Yarrow.

He promised me a milk-white steed,
   To bear me to his father's bowers ;
He promised me a little page,
   To 'squire me to his father's towers ;
He promised me a wedding-ring,—
   The wedding day was fixed to-morrow ;—
Now he is wedded to his grave,
   Alas, his watery grave, in Yarrow !

Sweet were his words when last we met ;
   My passion I as freely told him !
Clasp'd in his arms, I little thought
   That I should never more behold him !
Scarce was he gone, I saw his ghost ;
   It vanished with a shriek of sorrow ;
Thrice did the water-wraith ascend,
   And gave a doleful groan thro' Yarrow.

His mother from the window look'd,
  With all the longing of a mother ;
His little sister weeping walk'd
  The green-wood path to meet her brother :
They sought him east, they sought him west,
  They sought him all the forest thorough ;
They only saw the cloud of night,
  They only heard the roar of Yarrow !

No longer from thy window look,
  Thou hast no son, thou tender mother !
No longer walk, thou lovely maid !
  Alas, thou hast no more a brother !
No longer seek him east or west,
  And search no more the forest thorough ;
For, wandering in the night so dark,
  He fell a lifeless corpse in Yarrow.

The tear shall never leave my cheek
  No other youth shall be my marrow ;
I'll seek thy body in the stream
  And then with thee I'll sleep in Yarrow.
The tear did never leave her cheek,
  No other youth became her marrow ;
She found his body in the stream,
  And now with him she sleeps in Yarrow.

ODE

On the death of a young woman, Mary Miller, the nurse of the poet when a child. This young woman died from fever, and Alexander Bruce, the poet's father, buried her in his own grave.

THE peace of Heaven attend thy shade,
My early friend, my favourite maid !
When life was new, companions gay.
We hail'd the morning of our day.

Ah, with what joy did I behold
The flower of beauty fair untold !
And fear'd no storm to blast thy bloom,
Or bring thee to an early tomb !

Untimely gone ! for ever fled
The roses of the cheek so red !
Th' affection warm, the temper mild,
The sweetness that in sorrow smil'd.

Alas ! the cheek where beauty glow'd,
The heart where goodness overflow'd,
A clod amid the valley lies,
And " dust to dust " the mourner cries.

O from thy kindred early torn,
And to thy grave untimely borne !
Vanish'd for ever from my view,
Thou sister of my soul, adieu !

Fair with my first ideas twin'd,
Thine image oft will meet my mind ;
And while Remembrance brings thee near,
Affection sad will drop a tear.

How oft does Sorrow bend the head,
Before we dwell among the dead !
Scarce in the years of manly prime,
I've often wept the wrecks of time.

What tragic tears bedew the eye !
What deaths we suffer ere we die !
Our broken friendships we deplore,
And loves of youth that are no more !

No after-friendship e'er can raise
Th'endearments of our early days ;
And ne'er the heart such fondness prove,
As when it first began to love.

Affection dies, a vernal flower ;
And love, the blossom of an hour ;
The spring of Fancy needs control
To keep the beauty of the soul.

Versed in the commerce of deceit,
How soon the heart forgets to beat !
The blood runs cold at Int'rest's call :—
They look with equal eyes on all.

Lest lovely Nature be expell'd,
And friendship so romantic held ;
Then Prudence comes with hundred eyes :—
The Veil is rent ; the Vision flies.

The dear Illusions will not last ;
The aera of Enchantment's past ;
The wild Romance of Life is done ;
The real History is begun.

207

The Sallies of the Soul are o'er
The Feast of Fancy is no more ;
And ill the banquet is supply'd
By form, by gravity, by pride.

Ye Gods ! whatever ye withhold,
Let my affections ne'er grow old :
Ne'er may the human glow depart,
Nor Nature yield to frigid Art !

Still may the generous bosom burn,
Tho' doom'd to bleed o'er Beauty's urn ;
And still the friendly face appear,
Tho' moistened with a tender tear !

ODE

TO WOMEN

Ye Virgins ! fond to be admir'd,
With mighty rage of conquest fir'd,
   And universal sway ;
Who heave th'uncover'd bosom high,
And roll a fond, inviting eye,
   On all the circle gay !

You miss the fine and secret art
To win the castle of the heart,
   For which you all contend ;
The coxcomb tribe may crowd your train,
But you will never, never gain
   A lover, or a friend.

If this your passion, this your praise
To shine, to dazzle, and to blaze,
    You may be call'd divine :
But not a youth beneath the sky
Will say in secret, with a sigh,
    " O were that Maiden mine ! "

You marshal, brilliant, from the box,
Fans, feathers, diamonds, castled locks
    Your magazine of arms ;
But 'tis the sweet sequester'd walk,
The whispering hour, the tender talk,
    That gives your genuine charms.

The nymph-like robe, the natural grace
The smile, the native of the face,
    Refinement without art ;
The eye where pure affection beams,
The tear from tenderness that streams,
    The accents of the heart ;

At times, to veil, is to reveal,
And to display, is to conceal ;
    Mysterious are your laws !
The vision's finer than the view ;
Her landscape Nature never drew
    So fair as Fancy draws.

A beauty, carelessly betray'd,
Enamours more, than if display'd
    All Woman's charms were given ;
And o'er the bosom's vestal white,
The gauze appears a robe of light,
    That veils, yet opens, Heaven.

209   P

See Virgin Eve, with graces bland,
Fresh blooming from her Maker's hand
    In orient beauty beam !
Fair on the river-margin laid,[1]
She knew not that her image made
    The angel in the stream.

Still ancient Eden blooms your own
But artless Innocence alone
    Secures the heavenly post ;
For if, beneath an Angel's mien,
The Serpent's tortuous train is seen,
    Our Paradise is lost.

O Nature, Nature, thine the charm !
Thy colours woo, thy features warm,
    Thy accents win the heart !
Parisian paint of every kind,
That stains the body or the mind,
    Proclaims the Harlot's art.

The Midnight Minstrel of the grove,
Who still renews the hymn of love,
    And woos the wood to hear ;
Knows not the sweetness of his strain,
Nor that, above the tuneful train,
    He charms the Lover's ear.

The trembling frame, the living cheek,
Where, like the morning, blushes break
    To crimson o'er the breast ;
The look where sentiment is seen,
Fine passions moving o'er the mien,
    And all the soul exprest ;

[1] Bruce's repeated line.

Your beauties these : with these you shine,
And reign on high by right divine,
    The sovereigns of the world ;
Then to your court the nations flow ;
The Muse with flowers the Path will strew,[1]
    Where Venus' car is hurl'd.

From dazzling deluges of snow,
From Summer noon's meridan glow,
    We turn our aching eye,
To Nature's robe of vernal green,
To the blue curtain all serene,
    Of an Autumnal sky.

The favourite tree of Beauty's Queen,
Behold the Myrtle's modest green,
    The Virgin of the grove !
Soft from the circlet of her star,
The tender turtles draw the car
    Of Venus and of Love.

The growing charm invites the eye,
See morning gradual paint the sky
    With purple and with gold !
See Spring approach with sweet delay ! [2]
See rosebuds open to the ray,
    And leaf by leaf unfold !

We love th'alluring line of grace,
That leads the eye a wanton chase
    And lets the fancy rove ;
The walk of Beauty ever bends,
And still begins but never ends
    The labyrinth of love.

[1] Again Bruce refers to his favourite walk by the hill-foot, which charmed him so much, now known as " Bruce's path."

[2] See "Vernal Ode," which begins, "See, see, the genial spring again."

The Zone of Venus, heavenly-fine,
Is Nature's handy-work divine,
   And not the web of Art ;
And they who wear it never know
To what enchanting charm they owe
   The empire of the heart.

   Those who peruse Bruce's writings can easily recog-
nise *his* sentiments in these lines :

   " The sweet sequester'd walk."
   " The Muse with flowers the Path will strew."
   " See Spring approach with sweet delay."
   " O Nature, Nature, thine the charm."
   " Thy accents win my heart."

OSSIAN'S HYMN

TO THE SUN

O THOU whose beams the sea-girt earth array,
King of the Sky, and Father of the Day !
O Sun ! what fountain, hid from human eyes,
Supplies thy circle round the radiant skies,
For ever burning and for ever bright
With Heaven's pure fire, and everlasting light ?
What awful beauty in thy face appears !
Immortal youth, beyond the power of years !

When gloomy Darkness to thy reign resigns,
And from the gates of Morn thy glory shines,
The conscious stars are put to sudden flight,
And all the planets hide their heads in night ;
The Queen of Heaven forsakes th'ethereal plain,
To sink inglorious in the Western Main.
The clouds refulgent deck thy golden throne,
High in the Heavens, immortal and alone !
Who can abide the brightness of thy face ?
Or who attend thee in thy rapid race ?
The mountain-oaks, like their own leaves, decay ;
Themselves the mountains wear with age away ;
The boundless main, that rolls from land to land,
Lessens at times, and leaves a waste of sand ;
The silver Moon, refulgent lamp of night,
Is lost in Heaven, and emptied of her light :
But thou for ever shalt endure the same,
Thy light eternal, and unspent thy flame.

When tempests with their train impend on high,
Darken the day, and load the labouring sky ;
When Heaven's wide convex glows with lightnings dire,
All æther flaming and all earth on fire ;
When loud and long the deep-mouth'd thunder rolls,
And peals on peals redoubled rend the poles ;
If from the opening clouds thy form appears,
Her wonted charm the face of Nature wears ;
Thy beauteus orb restores departed day,
Looks from the sky, and laughs the storm away.

" Ossian's Hymns " are easily claimed for Bruce.
David Pearson, his familiar friend, knew of them, for
Bruce had explained to him what these were while he
was writing them.

ODE

WRITTEN IN SPRING

No longer hoary Winter reigns,
No longer binds the streams in chains,
    Or heaps with snow the meads ;
Array'd with robe of rainbow-dye
At last the Spring appears on high,
And, smiling over earth and sky,
    Her new creation leads.

The snows confess a warmer ray,
The loosen'd streamlet loves to stray
    And echo down the dale ;
The hills uplift their summits green,
The vales more verdant spread between
The cushet in the wood unseen
    Coos ceaseless to the gale.

The rainbow arching woos the eye
With all the colours of the sky,
    With all the pride of Spring ;
Now heaven descends in sunny showers,
The sodden fields put on the flowers,
The green leaves wave upon the bowers,
    And birds begin to sing.

The cattle wander in the wood,
And find the wonted verdant food,
    Beside the well-known rills ;
Blithe in the sun the shepherd swain
Like Pan attunes the past'ral strain,
While many echoes send again
    The music of the hills.

At eve, the flowery path along,
The milkmaid shortens with a song
    Her solitary way ;
She sees the Fairies, with their Queen,
Trip hand-in-hand the circled green,
And hears them raise at times, unseen,
    The ear-inchanting lay.

Maria, come ! Now let us rove,
Now gather garlands in the grove,
    Of every new-sprung flower ;
We'll hear the warblings of the wood,
We'll trace the windings of the flood ;
O come Thou, fairer than the bud
    Unfolding in a shower !

Fair as the lily of the vale,
That gives its bosom to the gale
    And opens in the Sun ;
And sweeter than thy favourite dove,
The Venus of the vernal grove,
Announcing to the choirs of love
    Their time of bliss begun.

Now, now, the Spring of Life appears ;
Fair in the morning of thy years,
    And May of Beauty crown'd :
Now vernal visions meet thine eyes,
Poetic dreams to fancy rise,
And brighter days in better skies ;—
    Elysium blooms around.

Now, now's the morning of the day ;
But, ah ! the morning flies away.
    And youth is on the wing ;
'Tis Nature's voice, "O pull the rose,
Now while the bud in beauty blows,
Now while the opening leaves disclose
    The incense of the Spring ! "

What youth, high-favour'd of the skies,
What youth shall win the brightest prize
    That Nature has in store ?
Whose conscious eyes shall meet with thine
Whose arms thy yielding waist entwine ;
Who, ravish'd with thy charms divine,
    Requires of Heaven no more !

Not happier the Primæval Pair,
When new-made earth, supremely fair,
    Smiled on her virgin Spring ;
When all was fair to God's own eye,
When stars consenting sung on high,
When all Heaven's Chorus made the sky
    With Hallelujahs ring.

Devoted to the Muses' choir,
I tune the Caledonian lyre
    To themes of high renown :—
No other theme than You I'll chuse,
Than You invoke no other Muse :
Nor will that gentle hand refuse
    Thy bard with bays to crown.

Where hills by storied streams ascend,
My dreams and waking wishes tend
    Poetic ease to woo :
Where Fairy singers charm the grove
Where Grecian Spirits round me rove,
Alone enamour'd with the love
    Of Nature and of You !

Here again, a local feature is described, the old folk
had a belief that at certain times the fairies were wont to
dance and sing on this hill-side, though the sounds were
produced by certain winds, blowing over the hollow parts
of the hill.

SONG

THE day is departed, and from under the cloud
    The moon in her beauty appears ;
The voice of the Nightingale warbles aloud
    The Music of love in our ears :
Maria, appear ! now the season so sweet
    With the beat of the heart is in tune ;
The time is so tender for lovers to meet
    Alone by the light of the moon.

I cannot when present unfold what I feel
    I sigh—Can a lover do more ?
Her name to the shepherd I never reveal,
    Yet I think of her all the day o'er.
Maria,[1] my love ! Do you long for the grove ?
    Do you sigh for an interview soon ?
Does e'er a kind thought run on me as you rove
    Alone by the light of the Moon ?

Your name from the shepherds whenever I hear
    My bosom is all in a glow ;
Your voice when it vibrates so sweet thro' mine ear
    My heart thrills—my eyes overflow.
Ye powers of the Sky, will your bounty divine
    Indulge a fond lover his boon ?
Shall heart spring to heart, and Maria be mine,
    Alone by the light of the Moon ?

[1] The young woman here designated " Maria " was the theme of
Bruce's " Love Songs," at times varied with Peggie, Eumelia, etc.

ODE

TO SLEEP

Here we have the poet's sad experience recorded, as the rising sun began to dawn, seen from the small window beside his bed.

In vain I court till dawning light
The coy Divinity of night ;
Restless from side to side I turn,
Arise, ye musings of the Morn !

Oh, Sleep ! tho' banish'd from those eyes
In visions fair to Delia rise ;
And o'er a dearer form diffuse
Thy healing balm, thy lenient dews.

Blest be her night as infants rest,
Lull'd on the fond maternal breast,
Who sweetly-playful smiles in sleep,
Nor knows that he is born to weep.

Remove the terrors of the night,
The phantom-forms of wild affright,
The shrieks from precipice or flood,
And starting scene that swims with blood.

Lead her aloft to blooming bowers,
And beds of amaranthine flowers,
And golden skies, and glittering streams,
That paint the paradise of dreams.

Venus, present a lover near,
And gently whisper in her ear
His woes, who, lonely and forlorn,
Counts the slow clock from night till morn.

Ah ! let no portion of my pain,
Save just a tender trace, remain
Asleep consenting to be kind,
And wake with Daphnis[1] in her mind.

ODE

TO A YOUNG LADY

EUMELIA bright with beauty's glow
In conscious gaiety you go
    The pride of all the green.
Attracted groups in silence gaze,
And soft behind, you hear the praise
    And whisper of the lark.

In Fancy's airy chariot whirl'd,
You make the circle of the world,
    And dance a dizzy round ;
The maids and kindling youths behold
You triumph o'er the envious Old,
    The Queen of Beauty crowned.

Where'er the beams of Fortune blaze,
Or Fashion's whispering zephyr plays,
    The insect tribe attends ;
Gay-glittering thro' a Summer's day,
The silken myriads melt away
    Before a Sun descends.

[1] The pseudonym for Bruce's friend, Willie Arnot.

Divorced from elegant delight,
The vulgar Venus holds her night
    An alien to the skies ;
Her bosom breathes no finer fire,
No radiance of divine desire
    Illumes responsive eyes.

Gods ! shall a sordid son of earth
Enfold a form of heavenly birth
    And ravish joys divine ?
An angel bless unconscious arms ?
The circle of surrendered charms
    Unhallowed hands entwine ?

The absent day ; the broken dream ;
The vision wild ; the sudden scream ;
    Tears that unbidden flow !—
Ah ! let no sense of griefs profound
That beauteous bosom ever wound
    With unavailing woe !

The wild enchanter Youth beguiles,
And Fancy's fairy landscape smiles
    With more than Nature's bloom ;
The Spring of Eden paints your bowers
Unsetting suns your promised hours
    With golden light illume.

A hand advancing strikes the bell !
That sound dissolves the magic spell
    And all the charm is gone !
The visionary landscape flies :
At once th'aerial music dies ;
    In wild you walk alone !

Howe'er the wind of Fortune blows
Or sadly fevering Fate dispose
  Our everlasting doom ;
Impressions never felt before,
And transports to return no more,
  Will haunt me to the tomb !

My God ! the pangs of nature past,
Will e'er a kind remembrance last
  Of pleasures sadly sweet !
Can love assume a calmer name ?
My eyes with Friendship's angel-flame
  An Angel's beauty meet ?

Ah ! should that first of finer forms
Require, thro' life's impending storms,
  A sympathy of soul ;
The loved Eumelia of the mind
Will send me on the wings of wind
  To Indus or the Pole.

ODE

TO A MAN OF LETTERS

Lo Winter's hoar dominion past !
Arrested in his Eastern blast
  The fiend of Nature flies ;
Breathing the Spring the zephyrs play,
And re-enthron'd the Lord of Day
  Resumes the golden skies.

Attendant on the genial hours
The voluntary shades and flowers
　　For rural lovers spring ;
Wild choirs unseen in concert join,
And round Apollo's rustic shrine
　　The sylvan Muses sing.

The finest vernal bloom that blows,
The sweetest voice the forest knows,
　　Arise, to vanish soon ;
The Rose unfolds her robe of light,
And Philomela gives her night
　　To Richmond and to June.

With bounded ray and transient grace,
Thus, Varro[1], holds the human race
　　Their place and hour assign'd ;
Loud let the venal trumpet sound,
Responsive never will rebound
　　The echo of mankind.

Yon forms divine that deck the sphere,
The radiant rulers of the year,
　　Confess a nobler hand ;
Thron'd in the majesty of Morn,
Behold the King of Day adorn
　　The skies, the sea, the land.

[1] As already shown, on Bruce's return from Edinburgh University
he formed a society of young men for special study. To each member
he gave a pseudonym, and here that of his intimate, John Birrell,
is assigned " Varro."

Nor did th'Almighty raise the sky,
Nor hang th' eternal lamps on high
    On our abode to shine ;
The circle of a thousand Suns
Extends, while Nature's period runs
    The theatre divine.

Thus some, whom smiling nature hails
To sacred springs, and chosen vales,
    And streams of old renown ;
By noble toils and worthy scars,
Shall win their mansion 'mid the stars,
    And wear th'immortal crown.

Bright in the firmament of Fame
The lights of ancient ages flame
    With never-setting ray,
On worlds unfound from history torn
O'er ages deep in time unborn,
    To pour the human day.

Won from neglected wastes of time,
Apollo hails his fairest clime,
    The provinces of mind ;
An Egypt,[1] with eternal towers,
See Montesquieu redeem the hours
    From Lewis, to mankind.

No tame remission genius knows ;
No interval of dark repose,
    To quench the ethereal flame ;
From Thebes to Troy the victor hies,
And Homer with his hero vies
    In varied paths to fame.

[1] The finest provinces of Egypt, gained from a neglected waste.

The orb which ruled thy natal night
And usher'd in a greater light
    Than sets the pole on fire,
With undiminish'd lustre crown'd,
Unwearied walks th' eternal round,
    Amid the heavenly quire.

Proud in triumphal chariot hurl'd,
And crown'd the master of the world,
    Ah ! let not Philip's son,
His soul in Syrian softness drown'd
His brows with Persian garlands bound
    The race of pleasure run !

With crossing thoughts Alcides[1] prest,
The awful Goddess thus addrest,
    And pointing to the prize :
Behold the wreath of glory shine !
And mark the onward path divine
    That opens to the skies !

The heavenly fire must ever burn,
The Hero's step must never turn
    From yon sublime abodes ;
Long must thy life of labours prove
At last to die the son of Jove,
    And mingle with the Gods.

[1] A patronymic by which Hercules is often described.

224

THE LOVERS

A POEM

The lovers in the following poem refer to the son and daughter of two local lords, the son being the heir to " Lord Balfour of Burleigh Castle," near Orwell, the lady, the daughter of Arnot of the Castle on the east shoulder of the Lomond Hill, now known as " Arnot Tower." The lady escapes from her father's castle at night with her lover, but is observed, pursued, overtaken and brought home.[1]

HARRIET

'Tis midnight dark : 'tis silence deep,
My father's house is hush'd in sleep ;
In dreams the Lover meets his bride,
She sees her Lover at her side ;
The mourner's voice is now supprest,
A while the weary are at rest :
'Tis midnight dark ; 'tis silence deep ;
I only wake, and wake to weep.

The window's drawn, the ladder waits,
I spy no watchman at the gates ;
No tread re-echoes thro' the hall,
No shadow moves along the wall.

[1] " Scotland Well," is said to have been the place of rescue.   Hence it is described in a local work as the " Battle of Scotland Well."   It is alluded to in a local poem—viz.

> " So sigh'd Matilda on the morn
> She left ' gay Arnot's happy walls,'
> And with her Lord was fleetly borne
> To Burley's joy-resounding halls."

Q

I am alone. 'Tis dreary night,
O come, thou partner of my flight !
Shield me from darkness, fierce alarms ;
O take me trembling to thine arms :

The dogs howl dismal on the hearth,
The raven croaks the dirge of death ;
Ah me ! disaster's in the sound !
The terrors of the night are round ;
A sad mischance my fears forebode,
The demon of the dark's abroad,
And lures, with apparition dire,
The night-struck man thro' flood and fire.

The *howlet*[1] screams ill-boding sounds,
The spirit walks unholy rounds ;
The Wizard's hour eclipsing rolls ;
The shades of Hell usurp the poles ;
The Moon retires ; the Heaven departs.
From opening earth a spectre starts :
My spirit dies—Away my fears,
My love, my life, my lord appears !

HENRY

I come, I come, my love ! my life !
And Nature's dearest name, my wife !
Long have I loved thee ; long have sought ;
And dangers braved and battles fought ;
In this embrace our evils end ;
From this our better days ascend ;
The year of suffering now is o'er
At last we meet to part no more !
My lovely bride ! my comfort, come !
The rapid chariot rolls thee home.

[1] The owl.

RUIN'D ARNOT

The ruins of a castle, a stronghold of the Arnots', once of great size
and strength, on the Lomond Hill, at the eastern extremity of the
Lochleven mentioned by the poet.

HARRIET

Now, without father, mother, friend,
On thee my future days depend ;
Wilt thou, for ever true to love,
A father, mother, brother prove ?
O Henry !—to thy arms I fall,
My friend ! my husband ! and my all !
Alas ! what hazards may I run ?
Shouldst thou forsake me—I'm undone.

HENRY

My Harriet, dissipate thy fears,
And let a husband wipe thy tears ;
For ever join'd our fates combine,
And I am yours, and you are mine.
The fires the firmament that rend,
On this devoted head descend,
If e'er in thought from thee I rove,
Or love thee less than now I love !
Altho' our fathers have been foes,
From hatred, stronger love arose ;
From adverse briars that threatening stood,
And threw a horror o'er the wood,
Two lovely roses met on high,
Transplanted to a better sky,
And, grafted in one stock, they grow,
In union spring, in beauty blow.

HARRIET

My heart believes my love ; but still
My boding mind presages ill :
For luckless ever was our love,
Dark as the sky that hung above.

228

While we embraced, we shook with fears,
And with our kisses mingled tears ;
We met with murmurs and with sighs,
And parted still with watery eyes.
An unforeseen and fatal hand
Cross'd all the measures Love had plann'd ;
Intrusion marr'd the tender hour,
A demon started in the bower ;
If, like the past, the future run,
And my dark day is but begun,
What clouds may hang above my head ?
What tears may I have yet to shed ?

HENRY

O do not wound that gentle breast,
Nor sink, with fancied ills opprest ;
For softness, sweetness, all thou art,
And love is virtue in thy heart.
That bosom ne'er shall heave again
But to the poet's tender strain ;
And never more these eyes o'erflow
But for a hapless lover's woe.
Long on the ocean tempest-tost,
At last we gain the happy coast,
And safe recount upon the shore
Our sufferings past and dangers o'er ;
Past scenes ; the woes we wept erewhile
Will make our future minutes smile ;
When sudden joy from sorrow springs,
How the heart thrills thro' all its strings !

HARRIET

My father's castle springs to sight ;
Ye towers that gave me to the light !

O hills ! O vales ! where I have play'd ;
Ye woods, that wrapt me in your shade !
O scenes I've often wandered o'er !
O scenes I shall behold no more !
I take a long, last, lingering view :
Adieu ! my native land, adieu !
O father, mother, brother dear !
Upon whose knees I've sat and smiled,
Whose griefs my blandishments beguiled ;
Whom I forsake in sorrows old,
Whom I shall never more behold !
Farewell, my friends, a long farewell,
Till time shall toll the funeral knell !

HENRY

Thy friends, thy father's house resign ;
My friends, my house, my all is thine,
Awake, arise, my wedded wife,
To higher thoughts and happier life !
For thee the marriage feast is spread,
For thee the virgins deck the bed ;
The star of Venus shines above,
And all thy future life is love.
They rise, the dear domestic hours !
The May of Love unfolds her flowers ;
Youth, beauty, pleasure spread the feast,
And friendship sits a constant guest ;
In cheerful peace the morn ascends,
In wine and love the evening ends ;
At distance grandeur sheds a ray,
To gild the evening of our day.

Connubial love has dearer names,
And finer ties, and sweeter claims,
Than e'er unwedded hearts can feel,
Than wedded hearts can e'er reveal ;

Pure, as the charities above,
Rise the sweet sympathies of love ;
And closer cords than those of life
Unite the husband to the wife.
Like Cherubs new-come from the skies
Henrys and Harriets round us rise ;
And playing wanton in the hall,
With accent sweet their parents call ;
To your fair images I run,
You clasp the husband in the son ;
O how the mother's heart will bound !
O how the father's joy be crown'd !

OLD FREESTONE " QUERN "
Found at Kilmagad, Portmoak. Supposed to have been used by
the monks for grinding corn. Seen in cottage.

A TALE

The theme of this poem was a favourite with Bruce. The scene is laid in the old and famous " Castle of Cleish," seen from the " Lomond Hill," westward. He would, no doubt, be familiar with the ballad, " King Malcolm and Sir Colvine," and knew well Sir David Lindsay's poem of " Squire Meldrum of Cleish." Thus he weaves Scottish history into his ballad.

WHERE pastoral vale renowned in song,
　　The limpid Gairney flows
In Caledonia's classic ground
　　The Hall of Arthur rose.

A nobler warrior never arm'd
　　To guard his native isle ;
A gentler friend did never make
　　The social circle smile.

Twice he arose from rebel rage
　　To save the Scottish crown,
And in the field where heroes strove
　　He won him high renown.

But to the plowshare turn'd the sword,
　　When bloody war did cease ;
And in the arbour which he rear'd,
　　He raised the song of peace.

An only daughter in his age
　　Solaced a father's care ;
And all the country blest the name
　　Of Emily the Fair.

The picture of her mother's youth,
  (Now sainted in the sky) ;
She was the angel of his age,
  And apple of his eye.

Something unseen o'er all her form
  Did nameless grace impart ;
A secret charm that won the way
  At once into the heart.

Her eye the pure ethereal blue,
  Than that did fairer show,
When'er she watch'd a father's look,
  Or wept a lover's woe :

For now the lover of her youth
  To Indian climes had roved,
To conquer Fortune's cruel rage,
  And match the maid he loved.

Her voice, the gentle tone of love,
  The heart a captive stole ;
The tender accent of her tongue
  Went thrilling thro' the soul.

The graces, that for Nature fair
  Present us mimic Art ;
The false refinements, that refine
  Away the human heart,

She knew not ; in the simple robe
  Of elegance and ease,
Complete she shone, and ever pleased,
  Without the thought to please.

233

Instruct th' unplanted forest-crab
   To leave its genius wild ;
Subdue the monster of the wood,
   And make the savage mild.

But who would give the rose a hue,
   Which Nature has not given ?
But who would tame the nightingale,
   Or bring the lark from Heaven ?

The father, watching o'er his child,
   The joy of fathers found ;
And, blest himself, he stretch'd his hand
   To bless the neighbours round.

A Patriarch in the vale of peace,
   To all he gave the law ;
The good he guarded in their rights,
   And kept the bad in awe.

Lord of his own paternal field,
   He liberal dealt his store ;
And call'd the stranger to his feast,
   The beggar to his door.

But, ah ! what mortal knows the hour
   Of Fate ?   A hand unseen
Upon the curtain ever rests,
   And sudden shifts the scene.

Arthur was surety for his friend,
   Who fled to foreign climes,
And left him to the gripe of law,
   The victim of his crimes.

A TALE

The Sun, that rising, saw him Lord
    Of hill and valley round,
Beheld him, at his setting hour,
    Without one foot of ground.

Forth from the hall, no longer his,
    He is a pilgrim gone ;
And walks a stranger o'er the fields
    He lately call'd his own.

The blast of Winter whistled loud
    And shrill thro' the void hall ;
And heavy on his hoary locks
    The shower of night did fall.

Clasp'd in his daughter's trembling hand,
    He journey'd sad and slow ;
At times he stopt to look behind,
    And tears began to flow.

Wearied, and faint, and cold, and wet,
    To shelter he did hie ;
Beneath the covert of this rock,
    My Daughter, let us die !

At midnight, in the weary waste,
    In sorrow sat the Pair ;
She chaf'd his shivering hands, and wrung
    The water from his hair.

The sigh spontaneous rose, the tear
    Involuntary flow'd ;
No word of comfort could she speak,
    Nor would she weep aloud.

In yonder hall my fathers lived,
  In yonder hall they died ;
Now in that church-yard's aisle they sleep,
  Each by his spouse's side.

Oft have I made yon hall resound
  With social, sweet delight ;
And marked not the morning hour,
  That stole upon the night.

When there the wanderers of the dark,
  Reposing, ceased to roam ;
And strangers, happy in the hall,
  Did find themselves at home :

I little thought, that thus forlorn
  In deserts I should hide,
And have not where to lay my head,
  Amid the world so wide !

A stranger, wandering thro' the wood,
  Beheld the hapless Pair ;
Long did he look in silence sad,
  Then shriek'd as in despair.

He ran, and lowly at the feet
  Of his late Lord he fell ;
Alas, my Master, have I lived
  To bid your house farewell !

But I will never bid adieu
  To him I prized so high ;
As with my Master I have lived,
  I'll with my Master die.

I saw the Summer-friend who shared
    The banquet in your hall,
Depart, nor cast one look behind
    On the forsaken wall.

I saw the daily, nightly guest
    The changing scene forsake ;
Nor drop a tear, nor turn his steps
    The long farewell to take :

Then to the service of my Lord
    I vow'd a throbbing heart ;
And in the changes of your life
    To bear an humble part.

Forgive the fond, officious zeal
    Of one that loves his Lord !
The new Possessor of your field
    A suppliant I implored.

I told the treachery of your friend,
    The story of your woe,
And sought his favour, when I saw
    His tears begin to flow.

I asked the hamlet of the hill,
    The lone, sequester'd seat,
Your chosen haunt and favourite bower,
    To be your last retreat.

I offer'd—what was all your own—
    The gold I had in store ;
Low at his feet I fell, and wept
    That I could give no more.

Your gold is yours, the generous youth
  With gentle accent said :
Your Master's be that little field,
  And cheerful life be led.

Now Heaven has heard my prayer ; I've wished
  I could in part repay
The favours your extended hand
  Bestow'd from day to day.

I yet may see a garland green
  Upon the hoary head ;
Yet see my Master blest, before
  I dwell among the dead !

In silence he look'd up to Heaven,
  And clasp'd his Edwin's hand
The eyes of Emily in tears
  Express'd affection bland.

From opening Heaven the Moon appear'd ;
  Fair was the face of night ;
Bright in their beauty shone the stars ;
  The air was flowing light.

Arthur resum'd the pilgrim's staff ;
  They held their lonely way
Dim thro' the forest's darksome bourne,
  Till near the dawning day.

Then a long line of ruddy light
  That quiver'd to and fro,
Reveal's their lone retreat, and closed
  The pilgrimage of woe.

He enter'd, solemn, slow, and sad,
    The destin'd hermitage,
A little and a lonely hut,
    To cover hapless age.

He clasp'd his daughter in his arms,
    And kiss'd a falling tear ;
I have my all, ye gracious Powers !
    I have my daughter here !

A sober banquet to prepare.
    Emilia cheerful goes ;
The faggot blazed the window glanced,
    The heart of age arose.

I would not be that guilty man,
    With all his golden store ;
Nor change my lot with any wretch
    That counts his thousands o'er.

Now here at last we are at home.
    We can no lower fall ;
Low in the cottage, peace can dwell.
    As in the lordly hall.

The wants of Nature are but few ;
    Her banquet soon is spread :
The Tenant of the Vale of Tears
    Requires but daily bread.

Like Nature's simple children here,
    With Nature's self we'll live,
And, of the little that is left,
    Have something still to give.

The sad vicissitudes of life
    Long have I learned to bear ;
But, oh ! my Daughter, thou art new
    To sorrow and to care !

How shall that fine and flowery form,
    In silken folds confined,
That scarcely faced the Summer's gale
    Endure the wintry wind ?

Ah ! how wilt thou sustain a sky
    With angry tempest red ?
How wilt thou bear the bitter storm
    That's hanging o'er thy head ?

Whate'er thy justice dooms, O God !
    I take with temper mild ;
But, oh ! repay a thousand-fold
    In blessings on my Child !

Weep not for me, my Father dear !
    The Virgin soft did say ;
Could I contribute to thy peace,
    O, I would bless the day !

The Parent, who bestows on all,
    For us will now provide ;
These hands shall leave the gayer arts
    Of elegance and pride :

What once amused a vacant hour,
    Shall now the day engage !
And Charity shall spread the board
    Of Poverty and Age.

At eventide, how blithe we'll meet,
  And, while the faggots blaze,
Recount the trifles of the time,
  And dream of better days !

I'll read the tragic tales of old,
  To soothe a Father's woes ;
I'll lay the pillow for thy head,
  And sing thee to repose.

The Father wept. Thy wond'rous hand,
  Almighty, I adore !
I had not known how blest I was,
  Had I not been so poor !

Now blest be God for what is reft,
  And blest for what is given !
Thou art an angel, O my child !
  With thee I dwell in Heaven !

Then, in the garb of ancient times,
  They trod the past'ral plain :
But who describes a Summer's day,
  Or paints the Halcyon Main ?

One day, *a wanderer in the wood*
  The lonely threshold prest ;
'Twas then that Arthur's humble roof
  Had first received a guest.

The Stranger told his tender tale :
  I come from foreign climes ;
From countries red with Indian blood,
  And stain'd with Christian crimes.

R

O may Britannia never know
   What these sad eyes have seen !
May an eternal veil be drawn
   That world and this between !

No frantic avarice fired my soul,
   And Heaven my wishes crown'd,
For soon a fortune to my mind
   With innocence I found.

From exile sad, returning home,
   I kiss'd the sacred earth ;
And flew to find my native woods
   And walls that gave me birth.

To church on Sabbath fond I went.
   In hopes to mark, unseen,
All my old friends, assembled round
   The circle of the green.

Alas, the change that time had made !
   My ancient friends were gone ;
Another race possess'd the walls,
   And I was left alone !

A stranger among strangers, long
   I look'd from pew to pew ;
But not the face of one old friend
   Rose imaged to my view.

The plow had razed the village green,
   Where we have often play'd ;
The axe had fell'd the hawthorn tree,
   The school-boy's summer shade.

One Maid, the Beauty of the Vale,
  To whom I vow'd my care,
And gave my heart, had fled away,
  And none could tell me where.

My cares and toils in foreign climes
  Were for that peerless Maid ;
She rose in beauty by my side :
  My toils were all repaid.

By Indian streams I sat alone,
  While on my native isle,
And on my ancient friends, I thought,
  And wept the weary while.

'Twas she that cheered my captive hours,
  She came in every dream,
As, smiling, on the rear of night,
  Appears the morning beam.

In quest of her I wander, wild,
  O'er mountain, stream, and plain ;
And, if I find her not, I go
  To Indian climes again.

The Father thus began : "My son,
  Mourn not thy wretched fate ;
For He that rules by Heaven's decrees,
  Makes life a mixed state.

The stream that carries us along,
  Flows thro' the Vale of Tears ;
Yet, on the darkness of our day,
  The bow of Heaven appears.

The Rose of Shaaron, king of flowers
  Is fenced with prickles round ;
Queen of the Vale, the lily fair
  Among the thorns is found.

E'en while we raise the song, we sigh
  The melancholy while ;
And, down the face of mortal man,
  The tear succeeds the smile.

Nought pure or perfect here is found ;
  But, when this night is o'er,[1]
Th'eternal morn will spring on high ;
  And we shall weep no more.

Beyond the dim horizon far,
  That bounds the mortal eye.
A better country blooms to view,
  Beneath a brighter sky. —"

Unseen the trembling Virgin heard
  The Stranger's tale of woe ;
Then enter'd as an angel bright,
  In beauty's highest glow.

The Stranger rose, he look'd, he gazed,
  He stood a statue pale ;
His heart did throb, his cheek did change,
  His faltering voice did fail.

[1] Bruce's words in his poem, " Elegy in Spring " has :

  " Rest in the hopes of an Eternal day
    Till the long night is gone."

At last, " My Emily herself
  Alive in all her charms ! "
The father kneel'd ; the lovers rush'd
  To one another's arms.

In speechless ecstasy entranced
  Long while they did remain ;
They glow'd, they trembled, and they sobb'd,
  They wept and wept again.

The father lifted up his hands,
  To bless the happy pair ;
Heaven smiled on Edward the beloved,
  And Emily the fair.

MONIMIA

AN ODE

In weeds of sorrow wildly 'dight,
Alone beneath the gloom of night,
  Monimia went to mourn ;
She left a mother's fond alarms ;
She left a father's folding arms ;
  Ah ! never to return !

The bell had struck the midnight hour
Disastrous planets now had power,
  And evil spirits reign'd ;
The lone owl, from the cloistered isle
O'er falling fragments of the pile,
  Ill-boding prophet plain'd.

While down her devious footsteps stray,
She tore the willows by the way,
   And gazed upon the wave ;
Then raising wild to Heaven her eyes,
With sobs and broken accents, cries :
   " I'll meet thee in the grave."

Bright o'er the border of the stream,
Illumined by a transient beam,
   She knew the wonted grove ;
Her lover's hand had deck'd it fine,
And roses mix'd with myrtles twine,
   To form the bower of love.

The tuneful Philomela rose,
And sweetly-mournful sung her woes
   Enamour'd of the tree ;
Touch'd with the melody of woe,
More tender tears began to flow.
   " She mourns her mate like me."

" I loved my lover from a child,
And sweet the youthful cherub smiled
   And wanton'd o'er the green ;
He train'd my Nightingale to sing,
He spoil'd the gardens of the Spring,
   To crown me rural Queen.

" My brother died before his day ;
Sad, thro' the churchyard's dreary way,
   We wont to walk at eve ;
And bending o'er th'untimely urn,
Long at the monument to mourn,
   And look upon his grave.

" Like forms funereal while we stand,
In tender mood he held my hand,
 And laid his cheek to mine ;
My bosom beat unknown alarms,
We wept in one another's arms,
 And mingled tears divine.

" From sweet compassion love arose,
Our hearts were wedded by our woes,
 And pair'd upon the tomb ;
Attesting all the Powers above,
A fond romance of fancied love,
 We vowed our days to come.

" A wealthy Lord from Indian skies,
Illustrious in my parent's eyes,
 Implored a mutual mind ;
Sad to my chamber I withdrew,
But Harry's footsteps never flew
 The wonted scene to find.

" Three nights in dire suspense I sat
Alone ; the fourth convey'd my fate,
 Sent from a foreign shore ;—
' Go where thy wandering wishes tend
Go, and embrace thy father's friend,
 You never see me more ! '—

" Despair ! distraction ! I obey'd
And one disorder'd moment made
 An ever-wretched wife ;
Ah ! in the circuit of one Sun,
Heaven ! I was wedded and undone.
 And desolate for life !

" Apart my wedding robes I tore,
And guarded tears now gushing o'er
   Distain'd the bridal bed :
Wild I invoked the funeral yell,
And sought devoted now to dwell
   For ever with the dead.

" My Lord to Indian climates went,
A letter from my Lover sent
   Renew'd eternal woes ;—
Before my Love my last words greet,
Wrapt in the weary winding-sheet,
   I in the dust repose !

" Perhaps your parents have deceived,
Perhaps too rashly I believed
   A tale of treacherous art ;
Monimia ! could you now behold
The youth you loved in sorrows old,
Oh ! it would break thy heart !

" Now in the grave for ever laid,
A constant solitary shade,
   Thy Harry hangs o'er thee !
For you I fled my native sky ;
Loaded with life for you I die ;
   My love, remember me ! "

" Of all the promises of youth,
The tears of tenderness and truth.
   The throbs that lovers send ;
The vows on one another's arms,
The secret sympathy of charms ;
   My God ! is this the end ? "

She said, and rushing from the bower ;
Devoted sought in evil hour
   The promontory steep ;
Hung o'er the margin of the main,
Her fix'd and earnest eyeballs strain
   The dashing of the deep.

" Waves that resound from shore to shore :
Rocks loud rebellowing to the roar
   Of ocean, storm, and wind !
Your elemental war is tame,
To that which rages in my frame,
   The battle of the mind ! "

With downcast eye and musing mood,
A lurid interval she stood
   The victim of despair ;
Her arms then tossing to the skies,
She pour'd in Nature's ear her cries,
   " My God ! my father ! where ? "—

Wild on the summit of the steep
She ruminated long the deep,
   And felt her freezing blood ;
Approaching feet she heard behind,
Then swifter than the winged wind
   She plung'd into the flood.

Her form emerging from the wave
Both parents saw, but could not save,
   The shriek of death arose !
At once she sunk to rise no more ;
And sadly-sounding to the shore
   The parted billows close !

ODE

WRITTEN IN THE COUNTRY IN AUTUMN

This ode was composed by Bruce, while residing at Forest Mill being among the last he is supposed to have written there. His mind was much affected by the state of his health, and his uncongenial surroundings, as his letter to his intimate friend, David Pearson, describes. All his home surroundings press in upon his mind, and these are seen in the reference, as the poem proceeds. The last two verses are very pathetic ; his own condition is foreshadowed. The place in the wood to which he often retired for contemplation is still pointed out.

'Tis past ! no more the Summer blooms !
    Ascending in the rear,
Behold congenial Autumn comes,
    The Sabbath of the year !
What time thy holy whispers breathe,
The pensive evening shade beneath,
    And twilight consecrates the floods ;
While Nature strips her garment gay,
And wears the vesture of decay,
O let me wander thro' the sounding woods !

Ah ! well-known streams ! Ah ! wonted groves
    Still pictured in my mind !
Oh ! sacred scene of youthful loves,
    Whose image lives behind !
While sad I ponder on the past,
The joys that must no longer last ;
    The wild-flowers strewn on Summer's bier,
The dying music of the wood,
And the last elegies of love,
Dissolve the soul, and draw the tender tear !

Alas ! the hospitable hall,[1]
   Where youth and friendship play'd.
Wide to the winds a ruin'd wall
   Projects a death-like shade !
The charm is vanish'd from the vales ;
No voice with virgin-whisper hails
   A stranger to his native bowers !
No more Arcadian mountains bloom,
Nor Enna valleys breathe perfume,
   The fancied Edin fades with all its flowers !

Companions of the youthful scene,
   Endear'd from earliest days !
With whom I sported on the green,
   Or roved the woodland maze !
Long-exiled from your native clime
Or by the thunder-stroke of Time
   Snatch'd to the shadows of Despair ;
I hear your voices in the wind,
Your forms in every walk I find,
I stretch my arms : ye vanish into air !

My steps, when innocent and young,
   These fairy paths pursued ;
And wandering o'er the wild I sung
   My fancies *to the wood*.[2]
I mourn'd the linnet-lover's fate,
Or turtle from her murder'd mate,
   Condemn'd the widow'd hours to wail ;
Or while the mournful vision rose,
I sought to weep for imaged woes,
   Nor real life believed a tragic tale !

[1] Arnot Tower.

[2] The pathway Bruce passed along on his way to where he herded
his sheep. It is still shown as " Bruce's Path."

Alas ! misfortune's cloud unkind
  May Summer soon o'ercast ;
And cruel Fate's untimely wind
  All human beauty blast !
The wrath of Nature smites our bowers,
And promised fruits and cherish'd flowers,
  The hopes of life in embrio sweeps ;
Pale o'er the ruins of his prime,[1]
And desolate before his time,
In silence sad the mourner walks and weeps !

Relentless power ! whose fated stroke
  O'er wretched man prevails !
Ha ! love's eternal chain is broke,
  And friendship's covenant fails !
Unbraiding forms ! a moment's ease—
O memory ! how shall I appease
  The bleeding shade, the unlaid ghost ?
What charm can bind the gushing eye ?
What voice console th'incessant sigh,
And everlasting longings for the lost ?

Yet not unwelcome waves the wood,
  That hides me in its gloom,[2]
While lost in melancholy mood
  I muse upon the tomb
The chequer'd leaves the branches shed ;
Whirling in eddies o'er my head,
  They sadly sigh, that Winter's near :
The warning voice I hear behind,
That shakes the wood without a wind,
And solemn sounds the death-bell of the year.

[1] Bruce's own condition when he wrote.
[2] This refers to a shaded spot in the wood at Forest Mill, to which he resorted for meditation.

Nor will I court Leathean streams
  The sorrowing sense to steep ;
Nor drink oblivion of the themes
  On which I love to weep.
Belated oft by fabled rill,
While nightly o'er the *hollowed* hill
  Aërial music seems to mourn ;
I'll listen Autumn's closing strain ;
Then woo the walks of youth again,
And pour my sorrows o'er th'untimely urn !

THE COTTAGE
Showing the upper portion at the time when the
poet died, 6th July, 1767

THE PARAPHRASES

There can be no question that spiritual songs formed an important part of the worship of the early Christian Church. The great Apostle to the Gentiles not only bade the early converts make melody in their hearts, speaking in psalms and hymns and spiritual songs—but gave a convincing proof of his belief in their sanctifying power when he and his companion in adversity awoke the echoes of the prison house at Philippi. The hymns and paraphrases written by Michael Bruce have frequently been referred to in the preceding narrative of his life and writings, and the circumstances which led Bruce into this species of composition are well-known.

The cause of sacred Hymnology was slowly moving forward in Scotland somewhat before Bruce's day. The Hymns and Spiritual Songs of Dr. Watts had originated a new movement in England, and this movement had been further advanced by Dr. Doddridge, the author, among other hymns of the second paraphrase, " O God of Bethel." It was still further promoted when it enlisted on its side the saintly genius of Cowper and the talent of John Newton, in the Olney Hymns. Slowly but surely the wave of grave sweet melody broke over the heart of Scotland. Ralph Erskine was one of the first to take up and locate the strain. His " Gospel Sonnets " were, in their day, the people's classic. These were written in a quaint style, and sometimes were dryly doctrinal. But Erskine was none the less a true " Makkar," and capable, when he did himself justice, of reaching a high level of poetic excellence. Bruce's Gospel Sonnets, however, may be placed in the front rank of their class.

After some years' consideration, the General Assembly of the Church of Scotland in 1781 adopted a collection of 67 hymns, which were from that time used in the

Church services. Bruce's sonnets consisted of two kinds, some wholly original, and others improvements on those already published. These form the second portion of the volume which Logan published while in London in 1781, of which there were three editions. In regard to these nine hymns it is sad to find that Logan pursued the same line of conduct as before with the poems, with this difference, that he begins with one by Rev. Dr. Doddridge, which the latter had published in 1745. Before entering on the full consideration of these, it may be well to call to mind the circumstances under which they were produced. Rev. Dr. Mackelvie tells us that a farmer named Gibson settled in Kinnesswood with his family, all of whom were fond of Church music. One of them took pleasure in teaching singing to those who cared to receive his instruction. Among these was a young man, John Buchan, who had been a member of this class. He afterwards resided elsewhere, and improved himself in this art. Returning to his native village he in turn set up a singing-class. Till then, the " old eight tunes " were alone used. Some even went so far as to say these eight tunes were all that should be used in congregational worship. They were named French, Dundee, Stilt or York, Elgin, Newton, London, Martyr's and Abbey (tunes). In the practice of song they were not permitted to use the Psalms, so some silly doggerel rhymes were employed. Buchan, who was aware that Bruce could and did write poetry, applied to him for a set of suitable words. Bruce complied with this request, and the verses he furnished being often used, the young folks became familiar with them, and thus they were afterwards able to verify what Bruce had written when seen among Logan's publications. It must be kept in view that at that period nothing but the Psalms were used in church. The evidence gained in this way became the strongest that under the circumstances could be desired. It resulted in two kinds of compositions which Bruce supplied—viz. some of the English hymns simplified and improved, and others that were entirely his own. Logan does not appear to have known this when he claimed them as his.

Someone has very truly observed that: " It is difficult to restrain one's indignation against plagiarism so base and audacity so supreme." Logan had to do with the issue of the Paraphrases in 1781. It is believed that there were other hymns by Bruce, but these had been so changed as to be beyond recognition. No doubt, Logan counted much on the death of Alexander Bruce, who lent him his son's MS. "poem book," but there remained others to witness against him. The absence of what Alexander Bruce termed " The Gospel Sonnets " in the 1770 volume of his son's poems gave rise to the thought that Logan was retaining these for a purpose.

A curious incident is said to have arisen in connection with the Paraphrases. For a long time it was supposed that Burns had been a contributor, and the manuscripts with his characteristically bold writing were adduced as a proof, but the writing was that of John Logan, whose caligraphy so resembled that of the national bard as to give rise to the supposition. As we have already observed, Michael Bruce deserves well of his country, as his writings, especially the Paraphrases, have been a source of comfort and inspiration to pious hearts at home and abroad.

THE ENTHRONED HIGH PRIEST

Hebrews iv. 14-16
(58TH PARAPHRASE)

WHERE high the heav'nly temple stands,
The house of God not made with hands,
A great High Priest our nature wears.
The guardian of mankind appears.

He who for men their surety stood
And pour'd on earth His precious blood
Pursues in heav'n his mighty plan
The Saviour and the friend of man.

Though now ascended up on high
He bends on earth a brother's eye ;
Partaker of the human name
He knows the frailty of our frame.

Our fellow-suff'rer yet retains
A fellow-feeling of our pains ;
And still remembers in the skies
His tears, his agonies, and cries.

In ev'ry pang that rends the heart,
The Man of sorrows had a part ;
He sympathizes with our grief
And to the suff'rer sends relief.

With boldness therefore at the throne
Let us make all our sorrows known ;
And ask the aids of heav'nly pow'r
To help us in the evil hour.

THE COMPLAINT OF NATURE

Job xiv. 1-15

(8TH PARAPHRASE)

FEW are thy days and full of woe,
  O man, of woman born !
Thy doom is written, " Dust thou art,
  " and shalt to dust return."

Behold the emblem of thy state
   in flowers that bloom and die,
Or in the shadow's fleeting form,
   that mocks the gazer's eye.

Guilty and frail, how shalt thou stand
   before thy sov'reign Lord ?
Can troubled and polluted springs
   a hallow'd stream afford ?

Determin'd are the days that fly
   successive o'er thy head ;
The number'd hour is on the wing
   that lays thee with the dead.

Great God ! afflict not in thy wrath
   the short allotted span
That bounds the few and weary days
   of pilgrimage to man.

All nature dies, and lives again[1] :
   the flow'r that paints the field.
The trees that crown the mountain's brow,
   and boughs and blossoms yield,

Resign the honours of their form
   at Winter's stormy blast
And leave the naked leafless plain
   a desolated waste.

[1] There is an old hymn by " Fowkes," on which part of the above
seems to be founded—viz.
    Alas, the meanest flower that grows,
    The vilest weeds that flourish in the field
    Revive in spring and bloom another year,
    But we the Great, the Brave, the Learned, the Wise,
    Soon as the hand of death has closed our eyes
    In tomb forgotten lie, no suns restore
    We sleep forever, sleep, to wake no more.

Yet soon reviving plants and flow'rs
   anew shall deck the plain ;
The woods shall hear the voice of Spring
   and flourish green again.

But man departs this earthly scene
   ah ! never to return :
Shall any foll'wing spring revive
   the ashes of the urn ?

The mighty flood that rolls along
   its torrents to the main
Can ne'er recall its waters lost
   from that abyss again.

So days and years and ages past
   descending down to night
Can henceforth never more return
   back to the gates of light ;

And man when laid in lonesome grave
   shall sleep in Death's dark gloom,
Until th' eternal morning wake
   the slumbers of the tomb.

O may the grave become to me
   the bed of peaceful rest,
Whence I shall gladly rise at length,
   and mingle with the blest !

Cheer'd by this hope, with patient mind,
   I'll wait Heav'n's high decree
Till the appointed period come
   when death shall set me free.

THE COMING OF THE MESSIAH

MESSIAH ! at thy glad approach
  The howling winds are still ;
Thy praises fill the lonely waste,
  And breathe from every hill.

The hidden fountains, at thy call
  Their sacred stores unlock ;
Loud in the desert sudden streams
  Burst living from the rocks ;

The incense of the spring ascends
  Upon the morning gale ;
Red o'er the hills the roses bloom
  The lilies in the vale.

Renew'd the earth a robe of light,
  A robe of beauty wears ;
And in new heavens a brighter sun
  Leads on the promis'd years.

The kingdom of Messiah come,
  Appointed times disclose ;
And fairer in Emmanuel's land
  The new creation glows.

Let Israel to the Prince of Peace
  The loud Hosannah sing !
With hallelujahs and with hymns,
  O Zion, hail thy King !

TRUST IN PROVIDENCE

ALMIGHTY Father of mankind,
  On Thee my hopes remain ;
And when the day of trouble comes.
  I shall not trust in vain.

In early years thou wast my guide
  And of my youth the friend ;
And as my days began with Thee
  With Thee my days shall end.

I know the Power in whom I trust,
  The arm on which I lean ;
He will my Saviour ever be,
  Who has my Saviour been.

In former times, when trouble came,
  Thou didst not stand afar ;
Nor didst thou prove an absent friend
  Amid the din of war.

My God, who caused'st me to hope,
  When life began to beat,
And when a stranger in the world,
  Didst guide my wandering feet ;

Thou wilt not cast me off when age
  And evil days descend ;
Thou wilt not leave me in despair,
  To mourn my latter end.

Therefore in life I'll trust to Thee,
  In death I will adore ;
And after death will sing Thy praise,
  When time shall be no more.

THE CALL OF WISDOM
Proverbs i. 20-31
(10TH PARAPHRASE)

In streets, and op'nings of the gates
    where pours the busy crowd,
Thus Heav'nly Wisdom lifts her voice
    and cries to men aloud :

How long ye scorners of the truth,
    scornful will ye remain ?
How long shall fools their folly love,
    and hear my words in vain ?

O turn, at last, at my reproof !
    and, in that happy hour,
His bless'd effusions on your heart
    my Spirit down shall pour.

But since so long, with earnest voice
    to you in vain I call,
Since all my counsels and reproofs
    ineffectual fall :

The time will come, when humbled low
    in Sorrow's evil day,
Your voice by anguish shall be taught,
    but taught too late, to pray.

When, like the whirlwind, o'er the deep
    comes Desolation's blast,
Pray'rs then extorted shall be vain,
    the hour of mercy past.

The choice you made has fix'd your doom ;
    for this is Heav'n's decree,
That with the fruits of what he sow'd
    the sinner fill'd shall be.

THE LORD GOD OMNIPOTENT
Job xxvi. 6-14
(9TH PARAPHRASE)

WHO can resist th' Almighty arm
    that made the starry sky ?
Or who elude the certain glance
    of God's all-seeing eye ?

From Him no cov'ring vails our crimes ;
    hell opens to his sight ;
And all Destruction's secret snares
    lie full disclos'd in light.

Firm on the boundless void of space
    he pois'd the steady pole,
And in the circle of his clouds
    bade secret waters roll.

While nature's universal frame
    its Maker's power reveals,
His throne, remote from mortal eyes,
    an awful cloud conceals.

From where the rising day ascends,
    to where it sets in night,
He compasses the floods with bounds,
    and checks their threat'ning might.

The pillars that support the sky
    tremble at his rebuke ;
Through all its caverns quakes the earth,
    as though its centre shook.

He brings the waters from their beds,
    although no tempest blows,
And smites the kingdom of the proud
    without the hand of foes.

With bright inhabitants above
  he fills the heav'nly land,
And all the crooked serpent's breed
  dismay'd before him stand.

Few of his works can we survey ;
  these few our skill transcend :
But the full thunder of his pow'r
  what heart can comprehend ?

SORROW, NOT WITHOUT HOPE

1 *Thessalonians* iv. 13-18

(53RD PARAPHRASE)

TAKE comfort, Christians, when your friends
  in Jesus fall asleep ;
Their better being never ends ;
  why then dejected weep ?

Why inconsolable, as those
  to whom no hope is giv'n ?
Death is the messenger of peace
  and calls the soul to heav'n.

As Jesus dy'd and rose again
  victorious from the dead ;
So his disciples rise, and reign
  with their triumphant Head.

The time draws nigh, when from the clouds
  Christ shall with shouts descend,
And the last trumpets' awful voice
  the heav'ns and earth shall rend.

Then they who live shall changed be,
    and they who sleep shall wake ;
The graves shall yield their ancient charge,
    and earth's foundations shake.

The saints of God from death set free,
    with joy shall mount on high ;
The heav'nly host with praises loud
    shall meet them in the sky.

Together to their Father's house
    with joyful hearts they go ;
And dwell for ever with the Lord,
    beyond the reach of woe.

A few short years of evil past,
    we reach the happy shore,
Where death-divided friends at last
    shall meet, to part no more.

DYING IN THE LORD

(5th Hymn at end of Paraphrases)

This popular hymn Logan found in Bruce's MS. The nature of it did not commend itself to him. Yet it was under consideration of the Paraphrase Committee, and was adopted. For several generations, at home and abroad, it was a favourite, comforting the dying, being the expression of the Christian's hope. It exhibits the dying poet's simple faith, and his sublime anticipations. Its last request was granted to him, as he passed to the higher life.

THE hour of my departure's come ;
I hear the voice that calls me home :
At last, O Lord ! let trouble cease,
And let thy servant die in peace.

265

The race appointed I have run ;
The combat's o'er, the prize is won ;
And now my witness is on high,
And now my record's in the sky.

Not in mine innocence I trust ;
I bow before thee in the dust ;
And through my Saviour's blood alone
I look for mercy at thy throne.

I leave the world without a tear,
Save for the friends I held so dear ;
To heal their sorrows, Lord, descend,
And to the friendless prove a friend.

I come, I come, at thy command,
I give my spirit to thy hand ;
Stretch forth thine everlasting arms,
And shield me in the last alarms.

The hour of my departure's come ;
I hear the voice that calls me home :
Now, O my God ! let trouble cease ;
Now let Thy servant die in peace.

Proverbs iii. 13-17

(11TH PARAPHRASE)

As written by Michael Bruce. This formed part of his MS. volume,
and is what his relations and friends expected to find in the volume
published as his in 1770.

O HAPPY is the man who hears
Instruction's warning voice ;
And who celestial Wisdom makes
his early, only choice.

For she has treasures greater far
    than east or west unfold ;
And her rewards more precious are
    than all their stores of gold.

In her right hand she holds to view
    a length of happy days ;
Riches, with splendid honours join'd,
    are what her left displays.

She guides the young with innocence,
    in pleasure's paths to tread,
A crown of glory she bestows
    upon the hoary head.

According as her labours rise,
    so her rewards increase ;
Her ways are ways of pleasantness,
    and all her paths are peace.

Isaiah ii. 2-6

(18TH PARAPHRASE)

This is Bruce's improvement on what was published as Paraphrase
No. 28 of the 1751 edition, and adopted in 1781.

BEHOLD ! the mountain of the Lord
    in latter days shall rise
On mountain tops above the hills,
    and draw the wond'ring eyes.

To this the joyful nations round,
    all tribes and tongues shall flow ;
Up to the hill of God, they'll say,
    and to his house we'll go.

The beam that shines from Sion hill
   shall lighten ev'ry land ;
The king who reigns in Salem's tow'rs
   shall all the world command.

Among the nations he shall judge ;
   his judgments truth shall guide ;
His sceptre shall protect the just,
   and quell the sinner's pride.

No strife shall rage, nor hostile feuds
   disturb those peaceful years ;
To ploughshares men shall beat their swords,
   to pruning-hooks their spears.

No longer hosts encount'ring hosts
   shall crowds of slain deplore ;
They hang the trumpet in the hall,
   and study war no more.

Come then, O house of Jacob ! come
   to worship at his shrine ;
And, walking in the light of God,
   with holy beauties shine.

As published in the 1751 edition of the Paraphrases.

IN latter days, the mount of God,
His sacred house, shall rise
Above the mountains and the hills,
And strike the wond'ring eyes.

To this the joyful nations round,
All tribes and tongues shall flow ;
Up to the hill of God, they'll say,
To Jacob's God we'll go.

To us He'll point the ways of truth ;
The sacred path we'll tread ;
From Salem and from Zion hill,
This law shall then proceed.

Among the nations and the isles,
As Judge supreme he'll sit ;
And, vested with unbounded pow'r,
Will punish or acquit.

No strife shall rage, not angry feuds
Disturb these peaceful years ;
To ploughshares then they'll beat their swords,
To pruning-hooks their spears.

Then nation shan't 'gainst nation rise,
And slaughter'd hosts deplore ;
They'll lay the useless trumpet by,
And study war no more.

O come, ye, then, of Jacob's house.
Our hearts now let us join ;
And, walking in the light of God,
With holy beauties shine.

Genesis xxviii. 20-22

(2ND PARAPHRASE)

This hymn appeared in Bruce's MS. volume, as improved by him,
and is No. 2 of the Paraphrases.

O GOD of Bethel ! by whose hand
   thy people still are fed ;
Who through this weary pilgrimage
   hast all our fathers led :

Our vows, our pray'rs we now present
    before thy throne of grace ;
God of our fathers ! be the God
    of their succeeding race.

Through each perplexing path of life
    our wand'ring footsteps guide ;
Give us each day our daily bread,
    and raiment fit provide.

O spread thy cov'ring wings around
    till all our wand'rings cease,
And at our Father's loved abode
    our souls arrive in peace.

Such blessings from thy gracious hand
    our humble prayers implore ;
And Thou shalt be our chosen God,
    and portion evermore.[1]

[1] " This 2nd Paraphrase was a great favourite of the late Lord Strathcona, and towards the close of his life, never would those who were around him forget the emotion with which they heard him repeat, not many hours before he died—without error, pause, or confusion—the whole of the 2nd Paraphrase, so dear to Scottish hearts—' O God of Bethel." That great hymn, dearest of all hymns to our people throughout Scotland and the Empire, echoed down the arches of Westminster Abbey as they carried him to his rest. And they would remember another Scotsman, David Livingstone, the immortal of another continent. That Paraphrase, they were told, Livingstone, when lost and famishing in the desert, read aloud to himself under the scorching sun, just as, possibly, at the very same time Donald Smith was reading or repeating it on the waste of snows in Labrador. Thus these two great solitaries met in a Scottish hymn learned at a mother's knee."

PARAPHRASES

As written and published by Dr. Doddridge in 1745,
and is No. 45 in the volume of Paraphrases published
in 1751.

> O GOD of Jacob, by whose hand
> Thine Isr'el still is fed ;
> Who through this weary pilgrimage
> Hast all our fathers led.
>
> To Thee our humble vows we raise ;
> To Thee address our pray'r ;
> And in Thy kind and faithful breast,
> Deposit all our care.
>
> If Thou, through each perplexing path,
> Wilt be our constant guide ;
> If Thou wilt daily bread supply,
> And raiment wilt provide ;
>
> If Thou wilt spread Thy wings around,
> Till these our wand'rings cease,
> And at our Father's lov'd abode
> Our souls arrive in peace—
>
> To Thee as to our cov'nant God,
> We'll our whole selves resign,
> And count that not our tenth alone,
> But all we have, is Thine.

Isaiah xlii. 1-13

(23RD PARAPHRASE)

As improved by Michael Bruce in the 1751 edition of the Paraphrases

> BEHOLD my Servant ! see him rise
> exalted in my might !
> Him have I chosen, and in him
> I place supreme delight.

On him, in rich effusion pour'd,
 my Spirit shall descend ;
My truths and judgments he shall show
 to earth's remotest ends.

Gentle and still shall be his voice,
 no threats from him proceed ;
The smoking flax he shall not quench,
 nor break the bruised reed.

The feeble spark to flames he'll raise ;
 the weak will not despise ;
Judgment he shall bring forth to truth,
 and make the fallen rise.

The progress of his zeal and pow'r
 shall never know decline,
Till foreign lands and distant isles,
 receive the law divine.

He who erected heav'n's bright arch,
 and bade the planets roll,
Who peopled all the climes of earth,
 and form'd the human soul,

Thus saith the Lord, Thee have I rais'd,
 my Prophet thee install ;
In right I've rais'd thee and in strength
 I'll succour whom I call.

I will establish with the lands
 a covenant in thee,
To give the Gentile nations light
 and set the pris'ners free :

Asunder burst the gates of brass ;
   the iron fetters fall ;
And gladsome light and liberty
   are straight restor'd to all.

I am the Lord and by the name
   of great Jehovah known ;
No idol shall usurp my praise,
   nor mount into my throne.

Lo ! former scenes, predicted once
   conspicuous rise to view ;
And future scenes, predicted now
   shall be accomplish'd too.

Sing to the Lord in joyful strains !
   let earth his praise resound,
Ye who upon the ocean dwell,
   and fill the isles around !

O city of the Lord ! begin
   the universal song ;
And *let the scatter'd villages*[1]
   the cheerful notes prolong.

Let Kedar's wilderness afar
   lift up its lonely voice ;
And let the tenants of the rock
   with accents rude rejoice ;

Till 'midst the streams of distant lands
   the islands sound his praise :
And all combin'd with one accord,
   Jehovah's glories raise.

[1] A line of villages along the roadside in Portmoak were so termed, and Bruce introduces this, in reference to their various classes for the practice of song.

Published as one of the Paraphrases of 1751.

BEHOLD my servant ! see him rise
    exalted in my might !
Him have I chosen, and in him
    I place supreme delight.

In rich effusion on his soul,
    my Spirit's powers shall flow,
He'll to the Gentiles, and the isles,
    my truth and judgments show.

Peaceful and calm shall be the words
    which from his mouth proceed,
The smoking flax he shall not quench,
    nor break the bruised reed.

The feeble spark to flames he'll raise ;
    the weak he'll not despise :
Judgment he shall bring forth to truth,
    and make the fallen rise.

His heart shall not despond nor fail,
    nor ought shall him dismay ;
Till judgment in the earth he set,
    and islands own his sway.

He who spread forth the arch of heaven
    and hung its orbs on high ;
Who form'd the earth, and bade his power
    its tribes with breath supply ;

Thus spake the Lord : Thee have I rais'd ;
    my prophet thee install ;
In right I've called thee, and in strength
    I'll succour whom I call.

I with the lands establish will
    a covenant in thee
To light the Gentiles, and the blind,
    and set the pris'ners free.

I am the Lord, and by the name
    of great JEHOVAH known :
Idols shall not my glory share,
    nor mount unto my throne.

Lo ! former scenes, predicted once,
    conspicuous rise to view ;
And future events, thus foretold,
    shall be accomplish'd too.

Sing to the Lord a new made song :
    let earth his praise resound :
Ye who upon the ocean dwell,
    and fill the isles around !

Ye who inhabit deserts wild,
    or peopled cities throng ;
With humble Kedar's scatter'd tribes
    the joyful notes prolong !

Let all, combin'd with one accord,
    Jehovah's glory raise ;
Till, in earth's utmost bounds remote
    the islands sound his praise !

THE DIVINE AMBASSADOR

Behold th' Ambassador divine
    Descending from above,
To publish to mankind the law
    Of everlasting love !

275

On him in rich effusion pour'd
  The heavenly dew descends ;
And truth divine he shall reveal,
  To earth's remotest ends.

No trumpet sound at his approach
  Shall strike the wondering ears ;
But still and gentle breathe the voice
  In which the God appears.

By his kind hand the shaken reed
  Shall raise its falling frame ;
The dying embers shall revive,
  And kindle to a flame.

The onward progress of his zeal
  Shall never know decline,
Till foreign lands and distant isles
  Receive the law divine.

He who spread forth the arch of Heaven,
  And bade the planets roll,
Who laid the basis of the earth,
  And form'd the human soul.

Thus saith the Lord,—" Thee have I sent
  A Prophet from the sky,
Wide o'er the nations to proclaim
  The message from on high.

" Before thy face the shades of death
  Shall take to sudden flight,
The people who in darkness dwell
  Shall hail a glorious light.

" The gates of brass shall 'sunder burst,
  The iron fetters fall ;
The promised jubilee of Heaven
  Appointed rise o'er all.

" And lo ! presaging thy approach
    The Heathen temples shake,
And trembling in forsaken fanes
    The fabled idols quake.

" I am Jehovah ! I am one !
    My name shall now be known ;
No idol shall usurp my praise,
    Nor mount into my throne,"

Lo ! former scenes, predicted once,
    Conspicuous rise to view ;
And future scenes, predicted now,
    Shall be accomplished too.

Now sing a new song to the Lord
    Let earth his praise resound ;
Ye who upon the ocean dwell,
    And fill the isles around.

Let Kedar's wilderness afar
    Lift up the lonely voice ;
And let the tenants of the rock
    With accent rude rejoice.

O from the streams of distant lands
    Unto Jehovah sing !
And joyful from the mountain tops
    Shout to the Lord the King.

Let all combined with one accord
    Jehovah's glories raise,
Till in remotest bounds of earth
    The nations sound his praise.

" THE SONG OF SIMEON "

Luke ii. 25-33

(38TH PARAPHRASE)

As Michael Bruce improved it, from an old hymn,
first published in 1566

Just and devout old Simeon liv'd
    to him it was reveal'd,
That Christ, the Lord, his eyes should see
    ere death his eyelids seal'd.

For this consoling gift of Heav'n
    to Isr'el's fallen state,
From year to year with patient hope
    the aged saint did wait.

Nor did he wait in vain ; for, lo !
    revolving years brought round,
In season due, the happy day,
    which all his wishes crown'd.

When Jesus, to the temple brought
    by Mary's pious care,
As Heav'n's appointed rites requir'd,
    to God was offer'd there.

Simeon into those sacred courts
    a heav'nly impluse drew :
He saw the Virgin hold her Son,
    and straight his Lord he knew.

With holy joy upon his face
   the good old father smil'd ;
Then fondly in his wither'd arms
   he clasp'd the promis'd child :

And while he held the heav'n-born Babe
   ordain'd to bless mankind,
Thus spoke with earnest look, and heart
   exulting, yet resign'd :

Now, Lord ! according to thy word
   let me in peace depart ;
Mine eyes have thy salvation seen
   and gladness fills my heart.

At length my arms embrace my Lord,
   now let their vigour cease ;
At last my eyes my Saviour see,
   now let them close in peace.

This great salvation, long prepar'd,
   and now disclos'd to view,
Hath prov'd thy love was constant still,
   and promises were true.

That Sun I now behold, whose light
   shall heathen darkness chase,
And rays of brightest glory pour
   around thy chosen race.

As the hymns and paraphrases are based upon certain passages in the Word which we are told will never pass away, so the memory of Michael Bruce in this connection will be a never-fading blossom in Sacred Song throughout eternity.

BRUCE'S COTTAGE, KINNESSWOOD

Showing the upper portion, with improvements, as reopened in July 1906

THE MICHAEL BRUCE COTTAGE
ENDOWMENT FUND

The cottage where Michael Bruce was born still continues to draw to Kinnesswood many a visitor of importance who would not otherwise have discovered the village, around which this event has thrown such an abiding lustre in our literary annals ; and so the humble weaver's dwelling will remain for ever a shrine of genius, as an endowment fund was raised, sufficient for its upkeep and permanent preservation. Not only the " Ode to the Cuckoo," and " Elegy on Spring," but the Paraphrases especially, will form songs of praise in all generations. Michael Bruce's renown may be said to be perennial and immortal as the renown of other sacred song writers. In this respect Bruce owned that rare and mysterious gift, the universal appeal to all who suffer the usual vicissitudes of life, and as other great writers awaken interest, esteem and respect, Bruce arouses all these emotions, and adds to them affection and enthusiasm especially in connection with his " Ode to the Cuckoo." The scheme for the endowment of the cottage is wholly appropriate to the memory of the poet, and it is not surprising that the appeal, which we reproduce here, met with such generous and handsome response from admirers of the poet at home and abroad. For this reason we think it would be quite in keeping with the character of the Cottage Edition to reproduce the appeal which was so successful and the results of which exceeded all expectation. There is also interesting correspondence from some of the contributors to the fund, who, in sending their gifts, paid tribute to the genius of Michael Bruce. The appeal gives a very fair description of the cottage as it was in the days of Michael Bruce, and its appearance at the present time. The Visitors' Book in the cottage contains the names of visitors from all parts of the United Kingdom, as well as the Colonies, and there is a record of a visit to the cottage in October, 1872, by the Rt. Hon. John Bright, M.P., who was, at the time, at the zenith of his fame.

Mr. Robert Paterson as a person intimately acquainted with the chronicles of the village, acted as guide. After an hour or so had been spent in examining the " hallowed ancient grey biggin' " Mr. Bright expressed a desire to visit the old churchyard. After receiving instructions as to the way there he cordially thanked Mr. Paterson for his attentions, at the same time asking his name, as he felt deeply interested in the account he had given him of Bruce's early life and struggles. Mr. Paterson replied in Scottish fashion by saying, " that since he had got his name, it was but fair noo that he had his," at the same time handing Mr. Bright an old snuff mull with an old snuff spoon attached. Mr. Bright said nothing, but getting into the carriage and shutting the door he handed his card out of the window and with a benignant smile told the driver to proceed. Mr. Paterson's astonishment on reading the card, " The Right Hon. John Bright, M.P." may be easily imagined. The news of the distinguished visitor's presence flew through the village like wild-fire, and in a short time several flags were flying from prominent places, and a regular ovation awaited Mr. Bright on his return. But in this the villagers were disappointed. After leaving Kinnesswood, he had an interview with Mr. Arnot of Portmoak, and visited the churchyard there, when, after lingering for some time with apparent deep emotion over the hallowed ashes of the Poet, he drove round Lochleven and entered Kinross from the south.

Shortly after the renowned statesman's visit to the grave of Michael Bruce, an interesting article appeared in " Good Words," wherein the writer asked what it was that so deeply touched Mr. Bright in the young poet as to induce him to make this pilgrimage ? It was specially the belief that to him of right belongs the authorship of the immortal lyric " The Ode to the Cuckoo." At a gathering of literary men Mr. Bright had repeated the exquisite ode.

THE APPEAL

Reprinted from " The Kinross-shire Advertiser,"
18th March, 1922.

We heartily commend to all who love the sweet hymns and paraphrases on which they were brought up, and which to many have proved a source of comfort and inspiration through life, the appeal from Mr. James Mackenzie to create a substantial sum for the upkeep and care of Michael Bruce's Cottage. The life and writings of Michael Bruce are of more than local interest, his poetry displaying a delicacy of thought and beautiful simplicity of language, which have ever a charm for all readers, young and old alike, of a refined and cultivated taste. To pious hearts at home and abroad, it has been truly observed, his writings are precious and Michael Bruce deserves well of his country. Genius is not within the reach of all, but true piety is. It was a power in Bruce's life, and the value put upon it is seen in one of his verses :—

> For she has treasures greater far
> Than east or west unfold,
> And her rewards more precious are
> Than all their stores of gold.

His sacred poems have been a source of comfort to many in trying circumstances. Lines of these hymns are met with, carved on tombstones far and near. Sympathy is the soul of all goodness, and thus has Bruce represented the Son of God to us in one of his paraphrases in such simple words of love and encouragement as these :—

> Tho' now ascended up on high,
> He bends on earth a brother's eye,
> Partaker of the human name,
> He knows the frailty of our frame.

The following note appears in Mr. Mackenzie's " Life of Bruce " :—

"The 2nd Paraphrase was a great favourite of the late Lord Strathcona, and towards the close of his life, never would those who were around him forget the emotion with which they heard him repeat, not many hours before he died—without error, pause, or confusion—the whole of the 2nd paraphrase, so dear to Scottish hearts—' O God of Bethel.' That great hymn, dearest of all hymns to our people throughout Scotland and the Empire, echoed down the arches of Westminster Abbey as they carried him to his rest. And they would remember another Scotsman, David Livingstone, the immortal of another continent. That paraphrase, they were told, Livingstone, when lost and famishing in the desert, read aloud to himself under the scorching sun, just as, possibly, at the very same time Donald Smith was reading or repeating it on the waste of snows in Labrador. Thus these two great solitaries met in a Scottish hymn learned at a mother's knee."

Even the " Ode to the Cuckoo " has a note of comfort in it as we remember, when, repeating it to Mr. Robertson, father of Sir Forbes Robertson, in London over 30 years aog, he stopped us after we reached the verse :—

> Sweet bird ! thy bow'r is ever green,
>   Thy sky is ever clear ;
> Thou hast no sorrow in thy song,
>   No winter in thy year !

" Repeat that again," he said. " I wish to get it into my head to cheer me up when I am walking along Fleet Street."

With all this in our mind, we have no doubt whatever that our readers, far and near, will respond liberally to the present appeal. Contributions will be received by R. S. Young, Esq., Royal Bank, Kinross, or James Mackenzie, Esq., J.P., 2 Rillbank Crescent, Edinburgh, and duly acknowledged in the " Kinross-shire Advertiser."

No one, familiar with the life and writings of Michael Bruce and the scenes of his brief and early life, can but feel the sweet influence, charm, and peaceful atmosphere of the humble dwelling on the hillside, overlooking Loch Leven where he was born, hallowed by many dear memories which time will never efface, and few, we think, will be able to resist contributing something, more or less, for the objects we have in view.

MICHAEL BRUCE'S COTTAGE

We are indebted to the late Mr. R. Burns Begg, and Mr. David Marshall, Fellows of the Society of Antiquaries of Scotland, for the preservation of the humble cottage in which Michael Bruce was born on March 27th, 1746, and in which he died, 5th July 1767. Between 1860 and

1870 the ruinous condition of the building was long a source of much regret to the many visitors whom admiration for the poet's genius, and interest in his brief and blameless life, attracted to the spot, and a few more years of neglect at that time would have completely obliterated all traces of this object of not merely local but national interest. The many associations, which attach to all the scenes of Bruce's short career cannot fail to centre with peculiarly touching interest, and with a stronger and deeper effect in the lowly dwelling in which his pure bright genius dawned so gently and in which it set so prematurely. Everything, from the lowly dwelling itself to its humble, peaceful surroundings, bears testimony to the applicability of the quotation from Washington Irving by which the late Dr.Mackelvie (Bruce's biographer) so happily characterises it : " True nestling place of genius which delights to hatch its offspring in bye corners." Indeed no one can visit the spot without participating, to a greater or less degree, in the feelings which are pathetically and simply depicted by Dr. Huie in a sketch which he contributed to the "Olive Branch " of 1831, describing a visit paid by him to Bruce's birthplace. " On returning," he says, " to Kinnesswood from Portmoak churchyard where Bruce is buried, I attended my venerable guide (Mr. Birrell) to the lowly dwelling where the poet resided. We first entered the garden. ' This,' said Mr. Birrell, ' was a spot of much interest to Michael. Here he used alternately to work and to meditate. There stood a row of trees which he peculiarly cherished, but they are now cut down,' added the good old man, and as he said this he sighed. ' Here again,' said he, ' was a bank of soft grass, on which Michael was accustomed to recline after he became too weak to walk, and here his father would sit beside him in the evening and read to amuse him.' We next entered the house. I experienced an involuntary feeling of awe when I found myself in the humble abode where neglected worth and talents had passed away and died. The little square windows cast but a feeble light over the apartment and the sombre shades of evening (for the sun had now set) were strikingly in unison with the scene. ' There ' said my conductor ' auld Saunders used to sit at his loom. In that corner stood the bed where the auld couple slept in this the bed which was occupied by Michael, and in which he died.' The good old man's eyes filled as he spoke. I found it necessary to wipe my own. I was not ashamed of my tears. They were a tribute to departed genius and there was nothing unmanly in their flow.''

Not long after Dr. Huie's visit nothing remained of the objects of interest he refers to, but the little garden and the four walls of the house standing bare and roofless, with here and there a great unsightly gap in them. This was the condition of the house in the autumn of 1868, when it was purchased at the instance of Mr. Begg and Mr. Marshall with a view to its immediate and entire restoration. There was evidence then that the walls had been altered from time to time to suit the taste or convenience of the occupants, windows that once existed having been built up, while others had been broken out in their stead. In course of time there was no difficulty in restoring the house both externally and internally, exactly as it stood in the poet's time. It was evident when the poet was born that the house consisted of only one storey, and that his birth took place in the lower flat of the dwelling. The house was occupied by Alexander Bruce, the poet's father, until his death in July 1772— five years after the death of his gifted son—and the poet's mother continued to reside in the house until the close of her life in August, 1798. After that it was occupied by the family of Jas. Millar, Weaver Kinnesswood, by whose father it was purchased, a few years after the poet's mother's death, and who continued to occupy it until 1847, when it fell into disrepair. In one of the title deeds to the property—a disposition dated in Feburary, 1750—it is gratifying to find that the house is described as then being in the occupation of Alexander Bruce. In a circular soliciting subscriptions, dated Kinross, 21st June, 1875, with a neat photograph of the cottage at the head, it is stated, " The whole repairs (amounting in all to £81 11s. 2d.) have been completed, and in every respect the cottage is now exactly the same as when the poet died." The cottage was then vested in an Association of Bruce's admirers, of whom Mr. Begg and Mr. Marshall were the leading spirits under new Trustees. It has been made a repository for all the relics of the poet that can be collected, and cannot fail to be an object of deep interest and of much attraction not only to the inhabitants of the County but to the public generally. It is to hoped that the preservation to us of this interesting memento of Michael Bruce may enable us to realise more fully than we have hitherto done, the lustre which his poetic genius sheds around his native county, and we sincerely trust that our appeal will not be in vain.—J. G. B.

The following correspondence fully explains the position :—

EDINBURGH, 2, RILLBANK CRESCENT,

14th Feb., 1922.

MY DEAR MR. BARNET,—I have not heard of you for a long time though I am one of the few who remain who saw the first copy of the " Kinross-shire Advertiser " printed off, and long knew your father. Well, I am still on for what naturally concerns us both, viz., Michael Bruce. I think I have found a suitable man—a wounded soldier—to be a caretaker of this cottage. He is thirty-two years of age, does photo work,

and can do all that the Trustees want from such a man. But
while he would live in the under part of the cottage he requires
some furniture. We find the coals—which is a chief point.
The Cottage is dry now and can be made comfortable. Now
I hope that I am right in my opinion of the people of Kinross
and County that, if a suitable appeal was put in your paper,
we would soon find their love for the dear young Poet would
cause them to furnish a bed, &c., a table, a few chairs, and
other things necessary, a set of drawers, a press, &c., for a
humble but comfortable home, and get them to send them in.
The baker's cart is a good mode of getting such conveyed,
and Mr. Young would be the man to manage this. I am on
for raising a Capital Fund of say £300 to yield a little to aid
the Trustees to retain a caretaker and keep the place properly.
I wanted to have a place in Kinnesswood where visitors
could have a cup of tea and cake, &c., when they drive over
in summer-time. I would also like to see a Library fitted up.
I have already furnished a considerable number of books
which only want shelves put up, and our caretaker would look
after this department, and the nearer the Cottage the better.
I mean to make a desperate effort to get all this done, as I
would like so much to see the Trustees left with what will
enable them to keep the place in good order. The Museum
I filled up has much that is interesting and associated with
the Poet, while I want the Trustees to make rotating visits
to the Cottage, and thus keep the whole alive and proper.
Our first effort is to get the furnishing of the under part, and
if those who wish to aid us, as I have stated, would intimate
this to Mr. R. S. Young, Solicitor, Kinross, I fully rely on
your valuable aid in this respect. I remain, Yours sincerely,
(Signed) JAMES MACKENZIE.

W. DULWICH, LONDON, S.E., 21.

20th Feb., 1922.

DEAR MR. MACKENZIE,—I was very pleased to get your
letter this morning, especially as it conveyed the impression
that you were still well and hearty, in a vigorous state of

mind, and as enthusiastic as ever in your efforts to keep alive the sweet memories of Michael Bruce, in connection with his birth-place. I need only say that it will give me the greatest pleasure to support you in making an appeal, not only to Kinross-shire readers, but I should hope to give Clackmannan and Fife also the opportunity of responding to the appeal by getting the Editors of some papers in these counties to draw attention to the matter. To begin with, if you have no objections, I would like to insert the letter you have now sent me, although it is written in a personal strain, in the " Kinross-shire Advertiser," as the letter goes very fully into the matter of what you wish, and I should be delighted myself to sub-scribe five guineas towards the fund you have in view. With kind regards and all good wishes,—I remain, Yours sincerely,

J. G. BARNET.

Mr. Mackenzie replied that he would be glad if we published his letter, and it is now up to all of us to help him in the matter as much as possible. At the close of his letter he writes :—

" I desire to thank you so much for the very kind offer of help you have given ; it has driven the dark clouds away. I would be glad if you would insert my letter in your paper, but first send me a proof as some little change may be necessary, and I am grateful for your handsome offer of ' a starting subscription.' I hardly know how to thank you, this gives me hope and cheer. Glad to tell you your kind subscription of £5 5s. has brought me in other two such sums."

CORRESPONDENCE RELATING TO
THE APPEAL

The Trustees for the Michael Bruce Fund owe a deep debt of gratitude to the late Mr. James Gardiner, M.P. for Kinross and West Perthshire, who passed away in January, 1925, and as I had the privilege of very close friendship with him I wrote an appreciation of him for the " Kinross-shire Advertiser " at the time, giving an account of what he had done on behalf of Michael Bruce's memory. We can never forget the very valuable aid he gave at a time when the fund was flagging, in kindly offering an additional £50 to the fund as soon as it reached £250, to bring it up to £300. As a result of this, not only was this amount reached, but the trustees received nearly £100 in excess of the amount originally aimed at. The correspondence I had with Mr. Gardiner in connection with this, forms a beautiful testimony to what he felt in regard to Kinross-shire and its local poet, Michael Bruce.

Mr. Gardiner was one of the most genial, generous and unassuming of men, whose name will be held in affectionate remembrance by many in Kinross-shire.

To Mr. R. S. Young, Mr. Gardiner wrote on 4th April, 1922 :—

" When the appeal for the upkeep of the ' Michael Bruce ' Cottage reached me, I had not the full knowledge which I now possess. The more one learns about Bruce, and studies his writings, the greater the sympathy and admiration for the man and his works. In a county like Kinross, rich in historical and literary records, the name of Michael Bruce is not by any means the least on its list. The simplicity and beauty of his language, the appeal it makes to all that is best in Scottish character, the suggestiveness of the open-air, the blue sky, the singing of birds, and all that makes Kinross-shire beautiful and dear to its sons, whether resident in the county or further afield, should be an incitement to take full advantage of the present privilege of making sure that Michael Bruce's name will be maintained in everlasting memory in his own county, and especially in his own old home. I therefore enclose you a further £5 towards this memorial."

On 10th August, 1922, referring to the progress of the Michael Bruce Fund at the time, Mr. Gardiner wrote :

" DEAR MR. BARNET,—We have many things in common and none of them at the moment of greater interest than Michael Bruce's Cottage. I feel that your efforts, coupled with Mr. Mackenzie's, should result in something more definite than seems probable at the moment, and I am venturing to write a letter to the Editor of the " Advertiser," making a proposal to contribute the last £50 of the £300 we want if the balance is secured during 1922. I feel, unless a real effort is made, that dribbles of 5s. and 10s. will never give us the amount necessary to get on with the work, and unless we strike the iron when it is hot it might not mature."

Mr. Gardiner was held in high esteem in Parliamentary and Agricultural circles, and his interest in the highest intellectual and spiritual welfare of the community marks him out as a man of true character, of whom any constituency might well be proud to have as Parliamentary representative. His interest in the life and writings of Michael Bruce is thus easily understood, and his offer of further support to the Fund, which is for a high spiritual ideal, is the natural outcome of his desire to keep alive that faith in things eternal which have made Scotland so great in the history of the world. We cordially recommend what Mr. Gardiner writes at the close of his letter, from which we quote : " To read calmly and thoughtfully one of Michael Bruce's poems is sufficient to impel kind thought of the young poet who, in such humble circumstances, contributed so handsomely and materially to his county and country."

Practically the last letter that I had from Mr. Gardiner, in connection with the Michael Bruce Fund was dated 12th December, 1922. This letter was not published at the time, and a portion of it will now be of some interest :—

DEAR MR. BARNET,—You have been exceedingly good to me, and your action on the ' Kinross Advertiser " has been much appreciated by many of my friends as well as myself. We certainly have no reason to be ashamed of our efforts on behalf of the Michael Bruce Memorial. My only regret is that it is not on a larger scale, and something more substantial : and in the near future we may have the privilege of meeting and discussing with other friends interested, the whole situation, and then deciding whether we would be warranted in going further or not. I could wish I were a millionaire or some wealthy man, and then would be able to accomplish memorials of this kind without troubling the general public ; yet I think it is not altogether for good that one does a thing of this kind, but it is really better that the memorial should be shared in by the people of the countryside, and this is being done to a greater extent than we estimated.

Evidently Mr. Gardiner had a real affection for the life, character and writings of Michael Bruce.

LETTER FROM MR. J. LOGIE ROBERTSON, " HUGH HALLIBURTON "

The letter which I received from Mr. J. Logie Robertson gave me particular pleasure, as through the " Kinrossshire Advertiser " we had a literary connection for nearly half a century, and I am proud to claim him as a Kinrossshire man, for he was born at Milnathort on 18th September 1846, which was exactly a hundred years after Michael Bruce's birth. I would take this opportunity of paying a tribute of gratitude to his memory, as well as his literary genius, by quoting a few sentences from an

appreciation which Sir George Douglas, Bart., his friend
for over thirty years, contributed to the " Scotsman " in
June, 1922, at the time Mr. J. Logie Robertson passed away.

" It is perhaps not yet clearly recognised that the death
of James Logie Robertson (" Hugh Halliburton "), which, as
notified in ' The Scotsman,' occurred in Edinburgh on the
13th inst., in the seventy-sixth year of his age, has removed
from our midst, not only a man of singularly pure and lovable
character, but also the leading Scottish poet of the time.
For from the small group of interesting and accomplished
verse-writers now before the Scottish public, Logie Robertson
stood out as one who had something quite definite of his own
to say, and a way of his own of saying it. He was ambitious,
not of receiving lavish praise, but of performing good work.
His ' Horace in Homespun ' is a book which may be read with
relish, profit, and increasing attachment, not only by poetry
lovers in the widest sense, but by many who fall back before
the higher flights of song. Even if its kindly tone and its
moral teaching could be disregarded, it would still be worthy
of study as a fount of the Scottish vernacular undefiled. And
if we Scotsmen are indeed in earnest in our desire to preserve
and foster all that is best and most truly distinctive in the
national spirit, then I submit that this little masterpiece of
authentic song has a permanent claim upon our care."

My last communication with Mr. J. Logie Robertson
I regard as the happiest of all our correspondence, consisting of the most beautiful and charming letter on
Michael Bruce that can be imagined, and I have pleasure
in now quoting this :—

1 BRAIDBURN CRESCENT, EDINBURGH,
26th April, 1922.

DEAR MR. BARNET,—I would have written you sooner,
but for my infirmity I enclose half a guinea for the object
you have in view. Kinnesswood and Kinross do well to
cherish the memory of Michael Bruce. He is the most lovable
poet in all our literature. His characteristic notes are naturalness and cheerfulness. He is no fireside poet : the Lomond

Hill was his mountain of the Lord, rising over the mountain tops, he was, and is, the poet of Lochleven ; and his favourite resort was the little churchyard of Portmoak, by the roadside, where were gathered together most of his happy memories. There is no sorrow in his song ; even death is only a brief parting, soon over. He is often jubilant, as in the noble outburst of prophecy :—

> The beam that shines from Zion hill
>   Shall lighten every land ;
> The Prince that reigns in Salem's tower
>   Shall all the world command.

As long as praise is a part of adoration, his hymns will be sung.

Some years ago I wrote a sonnet-sequence on Milton and Michael Bruce ; it is my best expression of the love and admiration I have for the sweet minor poet of my native shire.

With kind regards to you and all my friends of Kinross-shire, I remain,

Yours truly, J. LOGIE ROBERTSON.

A NEW ZEALAND TRIBUTE

We have pleasure in referring to the contribution of five guineas to the Michael Bruce Cottage Fund from New Zealand. This was conveyed in an interesting letter to me, from Mrs. H. L. Hay, a daughter of the late Dr. John Guthrie of Milnathort—hence the particular local interest of the letter :—

" I well remember how greatly my dear father admired his poems and his undoubted genius. Uncle Gardiner (the late Dr. Andrew Gardiner) too, quoted from him in a letter he sent, which I value still—after my little son, Thomas Guthrie, died so suddenly.

> In every pang that rends the heart
> The Man of Sorrows had a part. &c.

I think it is a beautiful idea to restore his Cottage, and thus help to keep alive his sweet influences, for, apart from his genius, he was such a truly devoted Christian. One cannot but wish there were more such sincere characters in the World now, brave enough to be outspoken in the cause of truth. It is a troubled time, and yet one feels that God is not quite forgotten, but has many earnest workers striving with His help and guidance to stem the tide of evil all around us. It seems to me the times are drawing near when we may expect the signs of His coming again, and ' shall He find faith on the earth '—I wonder ? It is a great question, and our one consolation is the ' Lord is a stronghold in the day of trouble, and He knoweth them that are His.' . . .

I shall be very glad if you will accept the enclosed draft for £5 5s. for your fund. I would like to have a share in this for old times' sake, and also to show that even in far New Zealand the name of Michael Bruce is known and loved. I used to have a copy of his poems, but fear it must have gone in our landslip of 1886, when we lost our old home and possessions at one fell swoop."

TRIBUTE FROM SOUTH AFRICA

Sir William Hoy, who is the General Manager of the South African Railways, sent a handsome donation of £10 to the Cottage Endowment Fund, and when the effort was crowned with success I received from him the following very interesting letter, which gives some particulars of his connection and interest in the Kinness-wood district. Sir William was in this country with Lady Hoy and their daughter, in 1926, being one of the Delegates attending the Imperial Conference.

RAILWAY HEADQUARTERS, JOHANNESBURG,
18th August, 1922.

DEAR MR. BARNET,—I was very glad to receive your letter of the 26th ultimo on my return to Johannesburg, and to know that the necessary funds have been forthcoming to perpetuate the interest and to keep open the home of Michael Bruce. My grandmother lived in Kinnesswood for years, and, as a boy, I stayed there for some time. The church to which my people belonged was the established church of Scotland Well in the parish of Portmoak. I came to South Africa a young man, but most of my career has been spent in the Transvaal, and I have taken part in the varying vicissitudes of this beautiful country. It has all been extremely interesting. With many thanks for your letter and with best wishes,

Believe me,

Yours sincerely,

(Signed)   W. W. Hoy.

TRIBUTE FROM SIR JAMES GUTHRIE

We have pleasure in quoting from a letter from Sir James Guthrie, ex-President of the Royal Scottish Academy, dated April 5th, 1922. His father, Dr. John Guthrie, was a native of Milnathort, and author of a volume on Sacred Lyrics, as well as other books, highly appreciated during his lifetime, including the " Household of Faith." Sir James writes :—

" I often heard my father speak of Michael Bruce, never without regard for the tender beauty of the verse he left, and the sympathetic understanding of Nature that informs it all. Short as it was, his life well deserves commemoration, for the spirit of his work is that of one ' Who loveth best all things both great and small,' and that is a spirit wanted in this troubled world to-day."

297

TRIBUTE FROM
SIR FREDERICK C. GARDINER, LL.D.

In sending a handsome donation to the Fund, Sir Frederick C. Gardiner, LL.D., Old Ballinkinrain, wrote me a letter on 31st March, 1922, suggesting that the appeal should awaken wide interest, and we quote this part of his letter :—

" I am interested in the effort that is being made to pre-serve Michael Bruce's cottage. It is very many years since I saw it. I feel that this good work should be supported by a very large number of people in Scotland, but no doubt it would be impossible to bring it before the notice of large numbers. I have pleasure in enclosing you cheque for £5."

TRIBUTE FROM LOCHGELLY

Writing from the " Advertiser " office on November 1st, 1922, Mr. Alexander Westwater, now proprietor of the paper, wrote to Mr. Young :—

" I beg to enclose cheque from Mr. Small, Town Clerk, Lochgelly, also a personal cheque, donations to the Michael Bruce Fund. I visited the house at Kinnesswood recently in the company of Mr. and Mrs. J. G. Barnet, who were on a short visit from London, and of Mr. Mackenzie, to whose initiative, I presume. the endowment fund was due. It was indeed a privilege to view the house and its very interesting contents with Mr. Mackenzie as a guide. A most interesting collection of antiques is gathered there. In addition to the Bruceonia of the collection there is much bibliographia and other things of great interest to Kinross-shire folks. The nucleus of a shire museum indeed exists there ; this is an aspect that might be developed alongside the main objective. Mr. Small, who has a very close connection with the Bishop-shire from both his paternal and maternal side, sends best wishes for the success of the fund, and you also have mine."

The Old Crusie.

Old Iron Handle
on a room door
at the time the
Poet was born.

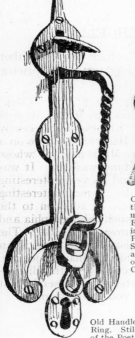

Old Handle on
the Door once
used by Mr.
Eben. Erskine
in his Manse,
Portmoak.
Still in use in
an upper room
of Bruce's
Cottage.

Old Handle and Risping
Ring. Still on the door
of the Poet's Cottage.

The Crusie (or Auld
Light).

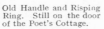

IN PRAISE OF " THE CUCKOO "

Mr. David Beaton, Newcastle-on-Tyne, in sending a welcome contribution of £1 to the Fund makes interesting reference to the Poet's environment. " Bruce and Kinnesswood," he considers, "are ' second to none in the annals of Caledonia,' and that even in the work of Scotland's National Bard one can find nothing more sublime than Bruce's ' Ode to the Cuckoo ' whose note I have heard many a time coming from the Bishop Hill." Mr. Beaton recalls the joys of " Kinaskit Market," fond memories of old family names in the Bishopshire, such as Birrell and More, who were identified with the famous vellum industry, being all records of the past worthy of preservation of the annals of Kinross-shire.

A MOST LOVABLE POET

I had an interesting note from Dr. J. M. Bulloch, who contributed the foreword to the book, " Scott and Goethe," written by the Rev. W. MacIntosh. M.A., Ph.D., Rector of St. Paul's Church, Kinross. As representing a high literary opinion, and describing Michael Bruce as a most lovable poet, the letter will form a fit conclusion to this correspondence. Dr. Bulloch wrote to me :—

" I am very much obliged to you for sending me the notes on Michael Bruce's Cottage. I have always been interested in Michael Bruce, for one of my earliest recollections was my mother's discussion of the Bruce-Logan problem. I agree with Mr. Logie Robertson that Michael Bruce was the most lovable poet of all our literature."

LIST OF CONTRIBUTORS TO THE
COTTAGE ENDOWMENT FUND

We have had ample evidence in the biography of Michael Bruce, which is now brought to a close, that the young poet in his life-time was a general favourite, and in response to the appeal for funds to keep his birth-place as a perpetual memorial, there is the same evidence that his memory is still held in universal esteem. In grateful acknowledgment to the subscribers, it occurred to us, as a remarkable record of this devotion to the life and works of Michael Bruce, to publish a list of those who so generously responded to the appeal. The names of many of the subscribers may be traced as having some local association, but on the other hand there are many subscribers whose names suggest that their admiration for Michael Bruce's poems has no such local connection. The list may not be complete, but it is thoroughly representative.

Sir Chas. E. Adam, Bart., Blairadam ; Messrs. J. L. Aitken, Kirkcaldy ; J. L. Anderson, Edinburgh.

Messrs. A Bruce, Glasgow ; W. Black, Kirkcaldy ; A. V. Begg, Edinburgh ; R. Brough, Bridge of Earn ; Rev. J. E. Black, Drum-chapel ; D. Beaton, Newcastle-on-Tyne ; D. Buchan, Alloa ; J. B. Black, of Tillywhally ; J. Barclay, Pittendreich ; Mr. and Mrs. J. G. Barnet, London ; Mr. and Mrs. Black, Kirkcaldy ; Mesdames Brydon, Edinburgh ; A. Blyth, Kennoway ; J. Blyth, Kinnesswood ; Miss Boddick, Miss Barnet, Edinburgh.

Lord Constable, Edinburgh, Sir John Clark, Edinburgh ; Sir John Cowan, Edinburgh ; C. Carlow, Esq., Edinburgh ; Mrs. M. Curtis, Scotlandwell ; Miss Connell, Edinburgh. Messrs. James Campbell, Middlesborough ; James Clark, Gospetry ; J. Campbell, Glasgow ; W. Campbell, Glasgow.

Rev. J. H. Dickie, Bearsden ; Messrs. J. Dickson, Galashiels ; Rev. Dunn, Glasgow ; Jas. Dow, Barby ; W. Davidson, Edinburgh ; Chas. S. Dougall, Dollar ; G. Duncan, Glasgow ; Mrs. Dalrymple.

The Earl of Elgin ; Dr. J. L. Ewing, Edinburgh ; Mr. Errol, Warminster.

Dr. Fergus, Glasgow ; Dr. W. Fowler, Edinburgh ; Messrs. W. P. Ford, Strathmiglo ; J. B. Fairgrieve, Edinburgh ; G. L. Fleming, St. Andrews ; Wm. Flockhart, Annacroich ; W. K. Falconer, Kinross ; Miss H. France, Alloa ; Mrs. Forfar, Milnathort.

Sir J. Guthrie, Row ; Sir F. Gardiner, Old Ballinkinrain ; Messrs. W. G. Gardiner, Stirling ; J. Gardiner, M.P., Dargill ; W. Gemmell, Glasgow ; J. Groundwater, Glasgow ; J. Gibb, Auchinleck ; J. Gray, Stirling.

Sir Wm. Hoy, New Zealand ; Messrs. G. Henderson, Glasgow ; J. Harvey, Edinburgh ; R. Haggie, Carnock ; J. G. B. Henderson, Linlithgow ; D. M. Hutchinson, Kinross ; Mrs. Hay, New Zealand.

Messrs. G. & J. Innes, Cupar ; Mr. Imrie, Kinross.

Messrs. J. B. Kinghorn, Nivingstone ; H. W. Kerr, Edinburgh.

A. Lowe, Esq., Edinburgh ; Misses Leishman, Edinburgh ; Lennox, Edinburgh.

Messrs. J. McKelvie, Oxford ; J. Mackenzie, Edinburgh ; J. F. Moncrieff, Edinburgh ; J. J. Moubray, Naemour ; A. McIntosh, Warroch ; G. Mackie, Edinburgh ; C. A. Mackenzie, Edinburgh ; H. P. R. Montgomery, Hattonburn ; G. Morgan, Stirling ; Morgan, Jr. J. Macleod, Edinburgh ; T. P. Marwick, Edinburgh ; G. R. McGibbon, Edinburgh ; Mesdames Mitchell, Glasgow ; P. McPhail, Edinburgh ; J. Murray, Greenock ; A. S. Morrison, Kinross ; McLaren, Kinross ; Miss Mitchell, Milnathort.

Sir M. Nairn, Bart., Kirkcaldy ; Dr. Nasmyth, Edinburgh ; Messrs. M. Nicol, Kirkcaldy ; A. Neale, Kinross ; Miss M. Nairn, Edinburgh.

Messrs. J. Platt, Edinburgh ; J. Phelp, Dundee ; Rev. J. F. Pollock, Portmoak ; Mr. and Mrs. J. Paton, Kirkness ; Mrs. W. Paton, Edinburgh.

Sir Wm. Robertson, Dunfermline ; Messrs. H. Reid, Edinburgh ; J. M. Ross, Kinross ; J. Logie Robertson, Edinburgh ; T. B. W. Ramsay, London ; Prof. D. Robertson, M.D., Edinburgh.

Major J. Simpson, Mawcarse ; Messrs. M. Sanderson, Galashiels ; J. N. Small, Edinburgh ; D. Storrar, Kirkcaldy ; Smith-Sligo, Oakley ; R. Small, Lochgelly ; Mesdames S. Sanderson, Galashiels ; H. Sanderson, Galashiels ; Steel, Edinburgh ; Misses Skinner, Edinburgh ; Steel, Edinburgh ; Sharp, Kinnesswood.

Messrs. J. Taylor, Edinburgh ; Wm. Tod, East Brackly ; A. Tweedie, Bo'ness ; J. Thompson, Kirkcaldy ; Mesdames Thomson, Cleish ; Troup, Edinburgh.

Messrs. R. Whyte, Chislehurst ; J. Moncrieff Wright, Kinmouth ; A. Westwater, Lochgelly ; R. S. Young, Kinross ; Mesdames M. L. Wright, Redcar ; M. Wright, Oban ; Misses Watson, Kinross.

COTTAGE ENDOWMENT FUND

List of contributors from whom donations were collected by Mr. Robert Haggie, an ardent admirer of Michael Bruce ;—

Messrs A. Allan, J. Adams, J. Addison, P. T. Bonar, D. Brown, A. C. Currie, D. Clark, Craig, P. Donald, A. A. Dawson, K. Dalziel, H. McDiarmed, W. D., J. Dick, W. B. Dow, F. Findlay, A. Fox, D. Gow, J. Gilmour, J. Glen, Miss M. S. A. Glen, D. H. Hoey, W. J. Inglis, W. Kirk, A. Mitchell, W. Mungall, M. B. Mitchell, J. Macgregor, J. Macara, Norval, J. Ross, J. W. Robertson, R. H. Robertson, R. Steele, H. R. Stewart, C. R. Shearer, Seath & Louden, J. Tulloch, H. A. Wacker, A. Wallace, Watt & Sons, J. M. Webster, J. Goodall, J. Harley, J. T. Spence, W. B. Robertson, Dr. and Mrs. Drysdale, W. Haggie, Netherhall, Dr. Tuke, A. McAlpine.